INSTRUCTOR'S MANUAL

INTRODUCTORY ECONOMETRICS

WITH APPLICATIONS

FOURTH EDITION

RAMU RAMANATHAN
University of California, San Diego

The Dryden Press

Fort Worth Philadelphia San Diego New York Orlando Austin San Antonio
Toronto Montreal London Sydney Tokyo

Address for Editorial Correspondence:
Harcourt Brace College Publishers, 301 Commerce Street, Suite 3700, Fort Worth, TX 76102

Address for Orders:
Harcourt Brace & Company, 6277 Sea Harbor Drive, Orlando, FL 32887-6777. 1-800-782-4479

Web site address: http://www.hbcollege.com

ISBN: 0-03-024829-9

Printed in the United States of America

0 1 2 3 4 5 436 8 7 6 5 4 3

TABLE OF CONTENTS

INTRODUCTION

This instructor's manual consists of some remarks about the organization of the class, solutions to the remaining problems, and general guidelines regarding the use of the ESL and ESLWIN programs. I would be grateful for comments about the text, "walk-through" applications, the ESL program, manual, and practice sessions, as well as notification of typographical errors. They may be e-mailed to *ramu@weber.ucsd.edu* or faxed to (619) 534-7040 or sent to the following address.

Professor Ramu Ramanathan
Department of Economics
University of California, San Diego
La Jolla, CA 92093-0508, USA

Please feel free to call me at (619) 534-6787 with comments and suggestions.

Organization of the Course

Chapters 1 through 10 constitute the basic topics in econometrics that most instructors would want to cover with varying degree of detail. If students have taken a prior course on probability and statistics, then Chapter 2 can be skipped initially. You can refer students to this chapter, as needed, when the relevant concepts are used in later chapters. If there is no probability or statistics prerequisite for this course, then Chapter 2 can be covered in more detail. Students should try to work out all the practice problems; they are usually short and the effort will be helpful in learning the subject matter better. By popular demand from students, I usually distribute the answers to ALL the Practice Problems (most of which are in this instructor's manual) so that they learn from the practice. There are plenty of exercises that can be used to test their knowledge.

Chapters 11, 12, and 13 are optional topics of a more advanced nature from which selections can be made as time permits. If the students are required to carry out an empirical project, it is recommended that Chapter 14 be assigned early. The entire book, including an empirical project, requires two quarters to do.

Practice Computer Sessions with the ESL and ESLWIN Programs

As mentioned in the text, the ESL program is easy to use, fast, and is designed to mesh coherently with the text. Professor Allin Cottell of Wake Forest University has graciously prepared a Windows interface which is available in the disk under the name ESLWIN. Appendix C has the details for the installation and usage of these programs. With them students can, without much help from the instructor, carry out the practice sessions described at the end of each chapter and reproduce all the examples and "walk-through" applications. The program is currently available only for MS-DOS machines. However, source code (written in the C programming language) is available (at a cost of $500) to adopters for transporting to other machines (contact the author directly).

Initial checking of the program

The first step is to check and make sure that the diskette is not defective. If the diskette appears to be defective, then send it to me and I will arrange to have a new one sent to you.

Documentations and Practice Sessions

Appendix C has details about how to install ESL and ESLWIN and carry out practice computer sessions. It also describes how users can set up their own data files and use these program. Also provided in this appendix is information about ready-made SHAZAM command files included in the disk. The author's Web site at *http://weber.ucsd.edu/˜rramanat* has links to the command files to reproduce the examples in the book using the internationally well-known program PcGive, developed by Jurgen Doornik and David Hendry of Nuffield College, University of Oxford, U.K.

Ready-made ESL command input files for obtaining the empirical results of the exercises in this manual are available in a diskette form. Contact me for a copy of the diskette (the Publisher does not have this).

ANSWERS TO REMAINING PROBLEMS

CHAPTER 1

EXERCISES

EX 1.1
We would expect ice cream consumption to depend on its price and how hot the day is. Income might also be important, but less so than the above variables. Thus, a possible specification is

$$\text{DEMAND} = \beta_1 + \beta_2 \text{ INCOME} + \beta_3 \text{ PRICE} + \beta_4 \text{ TEMP} + u$$

where DEMAND is the weekly consumption of ice cream (say, in gallons), PRICE is the price per gallon, INCOME is the average weekly income, and TEMP is the average of the daily high temperatures for the week. As temperature goes up, we would expect more people to buy ice cream and hence we would expect β_4 to be positive. If ice cream is more expensive, then demand would fall. Hence, we would expect β_3 to be negative. Finally, income effect is expected to be positive and hence β_2 is likely to be positive. If we obtain cross section data at a given point in time, that is, across individuals, then TEMP and PRICE will not vary across individuals and hence we cannot estimate the model. Therefore, time series data are more appropriate.

EX 1.3
An employee's salary would depend on the characteristics of the employee as well as the characteristics of the job. Thus, the list of explanatory variables should include EXPERIENCE, EDUCATION, AGE, GENDER, ETHNICITY, and OCCUPATIONAL TYPE. Other things being equal, we would expect wages to be higher for employees with more education and experience (that is, positive effects). When other variables are held constant, young workers might command less salary than older workers (positive effect). Occupational class is certainly important because an engineering job might pay more (given a fixed number of years of education and experience) than a clerical worker. If there is "discrimination" in the salary structure, ETHNICITY would make a difference. It should be

noted that OCCUPATIONAL TYPE and ETHNICITY are "qualitative variables", that is, are not readily quantifiable as EDUCATION or EXPERIENCE. Chapter 7 explains how such variables can be used in a regression context.

EX 1.4

There are two types of variables in a regression model, *independent*, and *dependent*. The "dependent variable" in a regression model is the attribute of an observation whose values we are interested in studying. An "independent variable" is an attribute that affects the value of the dependent variable. Thus, SQFT in Equation (1.2) is an independent variable that influences the price of a house. The nature of that influence is measured by the "parameter" β_2. A parameter is the *marginal effect* on the dependent variable of a unit increase in an independent (that is, explanatory) variable. Thus, β_2 in Equation (1.2) is the additional price (which is the dependent variable) for one extra square foot of living area, when YARD, BATHS, and BEDRMS are held constant.

CHAPTER 2

PRACTICE PROBLEMS

PP 2.1

The expected win is $\left[5000 \times \frac{1}{10000}\right] + \left[2000 \times \frac{1}{10000}\right] + \left[500 \times \frac{1}{10000}\right]$ $+ \left[0 \times \frac{997}{10000}\right] = 0.75.$

PP 2.2

The average stock should be $(1 \times 0.1) + (2 \times 0.25) + (3 \times 0.3) + (4 \times 0.2) + (5 \times 0.1) = 2.8$ dozens or 34 loaves of bread per day.

PP 2.3

To get the mean, multiply x by the corresponding $f(x)$ and sum over all values. For Table 2.1 we get $\mu_x = E(X) = (0.25 \times 0) + (0.75 \times 0.002) + \ldots\ldots + (3.75 \times 0.098) = 2.7855$. To get $E(X^2)$, square x, multiply it by $f(x)$ and sum over all the x values. This gives $E(X^2) = 8.06$. From this, we have, $\sigma^2 = E(X^2) - \mu_x^2 = 0.30098975$. Its square root is the standard deviation $\sigma = 0.54862533$.

By proceeding similarly for Table 2.3, we get $\mu_x = 506.25, \sigma^2 = 8415.9375$, and $\sigma = 91.738419$.

PP 2.4

We have, $\mu_x = E(X) = \left[0 \times \frac{16}{36}\right] + \left[0 \times \frac{8}{36}\right] + \left[0 \times \frac{1}{36}\right] + \left[1 \times \frac{8}{36}\right] + \left[1 \times \frac{2}{36}\right] + \left[2 \times \frac{1}{36}\right] = 12/36$. It is easy to see that μ_y also has the same value.

To obtain the variance, we first need $E(X^2)$ which is $\left[1^2 \times \frac{8}{36}\right] + \left[1^2 \times \frac{2}{36}\right] + \left[2^2 \times \frac{1}{36}\right] = 14/36$. Therefore, $\sigma_x^2 = E(X^2) - \mu_x^2 = \frac{14}{36} - \left[\frac{12}{36} \times \frac{12}{36}\right] = 10/36$. This is also equal to σ_y^2.

PP 2.5

$Cov(X, Y) = E(XY) - \mu_x \mu_y$. To obtain $E(XY)$ for Table 2.2, multiply the probability of each cell by the corresponding values of X and Y and sum over all the cells. The only nonzero entry is when $X = Y = 1$ with probability 2/36, so that $E(XY) = 2/36$. Therefore, $Cov(X, Y) = \frac{2}{36} - \left[\frac{12}{36} \times \frac{12}{36}\right] = -2/36$. From Equation (2.7), the correlation coefficient is $-(2/36) \div (10/36) = -0.2$.

EXERCISES

EX 2.1

This is the binomial distribution described in Section 2.1. From the formula given there we see that frequency distribution is given by the following.

x	0	1	2	3	4
$f(x)$	$\frac{1}{16}$	$\frac{4}{16}$	$\frac{6}{16}$	$\frac{4}{16}$	$\frac{1}{16}$

EX 2.2

When a pair of dice is rolled, there are 36 possibilities each with a probability of 1/36. X can take values from 2 through 12. $X = 2$ can be represented by the point (1, 1), where the first element is the outcome of the first die and the second element is the outcome of the second die. Hence $P(X = 2) = P(1, 1) = 1/36$. $P(X = 3) = P(1, 2) + P(2, 1) = 2/36$. By proceeding similarly, we obtain the frequency distribution of X as follows (this is known as a *triangular distribution*):

x	2	3	4	5	6	7	8	9	10	11	12
$f(x)$	$\frac{1}{36}$	$\frac{2}{36}$	$\frac{3}{36}$	$\frac{4}{36}$	$\frac{5}{36}$	$\frac{6}{36}$	$\frac{5}{36}$	$\frac{4}{36}$	$\frac{3}{36}$	$\frac{2}{36}$	$\frac{1}{36}$

EX 2.3

This is a binomial distribution with $n = 20$. Let X be the number of defective chips out of 20. We have $p = 0.1$. The computer will work if no more than 2 micro chips are defective. Thus, we need $P(X \leq 2) = P(X = 0) + P(X = 1) + P(X = 2)$. From Table A.6 we see that $P(X \leq 2) = 1 - P(X \geq 3) = 1 - 0.3231 = 0.6769$.

EX 2.5

Let X be the number of bulbs out of 20 (= n) that *do not* germinate. Then $p = 0.2$. My wife will not get a refund if $X \leq 2$. We therefore need $P(X \leq 2)$ for a binomial distribution with $n = 20$ and $p = 0.2$. From Table A.6, $P(X \leq 2) = 1 - P(X \geq 3) = 1 - 0.7939 = 0.2061$.

EX 2.7

$E(Z) = \Sigma_i (a + bx_i) f(x_i) = \Sigma_i a f(x_i) + \Sigma_i b x_i f(x_i) = a + b\mu_x$, because $\Sigma_i f(x_i) = 1$ and $\Sigma_i x_i f(x_i) = \mu_x$. By proceeding similarly, it is easy to verify that $E(Z^2) = a^2 + 2abE(X) + b^2 E(X^2)$. Therefore, $V(Z) = E(Z^2) - [E(Z)]^2 = a^2 + 2abE(X) + b^2 E(X^2) - (a + b\mu_x)^2 = b^2[E(X^2) - \mu_x^2] = b^2\sigma_x^2$.

EX 2.8

To obtain the mean of the binomial distribution given in the answer to Exercise 2.1, multiply each x by the corresponding probability and sum over all the entries. This gives the value 2 which could also have been obtained by noting that the distribution is symmetric around 2. To get $E(X^2)$, square each x first, then multiply it by the corresponding $f(x)$ and then sum over all x. We get $E(X^2) = 5$. The variance and standard deviation are now 1 and 1 respectively.

To obtain the mean of the triangular distribution given in the answer to Exercise 2.2, multiply each x by the corresponding probability and sum over all the entries. This gives the value 7 which could also have been obtained by noting that the distribution is symmetric around 7. To get $E(X^2)$, square each x first, then multiply it by the corresponding $f(x)$ and then sum over all x. We get $E(X^2) = 54.8333$. The variance and standard deviation are now 5.8333 and 2.4152 respectively.

EX 2.10

If the machine is rented for t hours, the revenue is $50t$, but it costs X^2 dollars because the machine breaks down periodically. The profit function is therefore $\pi(X, t) = 50t - X^2$. We are given that $E(X) = V(X) = 2t$. Hence expected profit is $E(\pi) = 50t - E(X^2) = 50t - [V(X) + \{E(X)\}^2] = 50t - 2t - 4t^2 = 48t - 4t^2$. From Appendix Section 2.A.3 we see that the condition for maximizing profits is $48 - 8t = 0$. Thus the optimum number of hours to rent is 6.

EX 2.12

2.4a $Var(aX + bY) = E[(aX + bY)^2] - [E(aX + bY)]^2$. The first term is $E(a^2X^2) + E(b^2Y^2) + E(2abXY) = a^2E(X^2) + b^2E(Y^2) + 2abE(XY)$. The second term is $a^2[E(X)]^2 + b^2[E(Y)]^2 + 2abE(X)E(Y)$. Grouping terms appropriately, we have $Var(aX + bY) = a^2 [E(X^2) - \{E(X)\}^2] + b^2 [E(Y^2) - \{E(Y)\}^2] + 2ab[E(XY) - \{E(X)E(Y)\}] = a^2Var(X) + b^2Var(Y) + 2abCov(X, Y)$. The special cases follow by setting $a = 1$ and $b = \pm 1$.

2.4c Let $f(x, y)$ be the joint density of X and Y, and μ_x and μ_y be the corresponding means. $Cov(X, Y) = E(XY) - \mu_x \mu_y$. Because of independence, $f(x, y) = f(x)f(y)$. Hence $E(XY) = \Sigma_{xy} xy\, f(x)\, f(y)$. But x and y are separable in the summation and hence we have

$$E(XY) = [\Sigma_x xf(x)]\,[\Sigma_y f(y)] = E(X)E(Y)$$

It follows therefore that the covariance is zero. Because the correlation coefficient has the covariance as the numerator, it is also zero. In this case, the covariance terms in 2.4a drop out.

2.4e $Cov(X, X) = E(X^2) - [E(X)]^2 = Var(X)$. It follows from this that the correlation coefficient between X and itself is 1.

2.4f For the first part, if $U = a_0 + a_1 X$, $V = b_0 + b_1 Y$, then $\mu_U = a_0 + a_1 \mu_x, \mu_V = b_0 + b_1 \mu_y$, $\text{Var}(U) = a_1^2\, \sigma_x^2$, $\text{Var}(V) = b_1^2\, \sigma_y^2$, and $\text{Cov}(U, V) = a_1\, b_1\, \sigma_{xy}$. It follows from the definition of the correlation that $\rho_{UV} = \sigma_{xy}/\sigma_x \sigma_y = \rho_{xy}$. To prove the second part, we need only a counter example. Let $U = X + Y$ and $V = X - Y$, where X and Y have each mean zero, the same variance σ^2, and covariance σ_{xy} ($\neq 0$). Then $E(U) = E(V) = 0$ and $Cov(U, V) = E(UV) = E(X^2 - Y^2) = 0$. Thus U and V are uncorrelated even though X and Y have the correlation coefficient σ_{xy}/σ^2.

EX 2.14

Each x_i has expectation μ and hence $E(\Sigma x_i) = n\mu$. It follows that $E(\bar{x}) = \mu$. From Property 2.A.5c, $Var(\Sigma x_i) = n\sigma^2$ because the x_i's are independent and identically distributed. Hence $Var(\bar{x}) = \sigma^2/n$. $E(y) = \frac{1}{n} \Sigma a_i \mu = \mu \frac{1}{n} \Sigma a_i$. For this to be equal to μ, the condition is $\Sigma a_i = n$. Also, $V(y) = \frac{\sigma^2}{n^2} \Sigma a_i^2$.

EX 2.16

The test statistic is $F_c = [(n-2)r^2]/[1-r^2]$, where $n = 26$ and $r = 0.37$. Under the null hypothesis of zero correlation, the test statistic has an F-distribution with 1 d.f. for the numerator and 24 d.f. for the denominator. From Table A.4a we note that $F^*_{1,24} = 7.82$. Also, $F_c = 3.807$ which is less than F^* and hence we cannot reject the null hypothesis.

EX 2.17

(1) The mean value of the houses is $\bar{y} = 107226/500 = 214.452$ thousands of dollars. The mean income is $\bar{x} = 24838/500 = 49.676$. The sample variances are given by Equation (2.11). The values are $66398/499 = 133.062$ for income and $1398308/499 = 2802.22$ for house value. The standard deviations are the corresponding square roots, namely, 11.535 and 52.936.

(2) The correlation between the two variables is given by Equation (2.13). We have

$$r_{xy} = \frac{194293}{(66398)^{½}\,(1398308)^{½}} = 0.638.$$

(3) Assuming that the sample houses are drawn independently from the same population, the confidence interval for the mean value of houses is $\bar{y} \pm [(s_y/\sqrt{n})t^*_{499}] = 214.452 \pm [(52.936/\sqrt{499})\ 1.96] = 214.452 \pm 4.645 = (209.807, 219.097)$.

(4) The test statistic is $F_c = [(n-2)r^2]/[1-r^2]$, where $n = 500$ and $r = 0.638$. Under the null hypothesis of zero correlation, the test statistic has an F-distribution with 1 d.f. for the numerator and 498 d.f. for the denominator. From Table A.4a we note that $F^*_{1,498} = 6.63$. Also, $F_c = 341.9$ which is greater than F^* and hence we reject the null hypothesis and conclude that there is a significant correlation between household income and the value of houses.

EX 2.18

We have, $n = 81$, $\bar{x} = 739.98$ and $s = 312.7$. From the t-table, $t^*_{80}(0.025) = 1.993$ (interpolating between 60 and 120 d.f.). The confidence interval for the mean claim is therefore, $739.98 \pm [(312.7/9)\ 1.993] = (670.734, 809.226)$. Because this confidence interval includes the value 800, we do not reject the null hypothesis that the population mean is 800. The assumption needed is that the sample claims be a random sample from the same distribution.

EX 2.19

The ESL commands for this exercise are given below.

```
smpl 1959 1970
corr unemp cpi wggr ;
smpl 1971 1980
corr unemp cpi wggr ;
smpl 1981 1995
corr unemp cpi wggr ;
```

The computed correlation coefficients for the three periods are as follows.

1959-70	corr(unemp, cpi) = -0.601
	corr(unemp, wggr) = - 0.637
1971-80	corr(unemp, cpi) = 0.340
	corr(unemp, wggr) = - 0.132
1981-95	corr(unemp, cpi) = -0.608
	corr(unemp, wggr) = - 0.425

There was a negative correlation between unemployment and the consumer price index in the first and third periods but not in the second period. The correlation between unemployment and wage growth, however, was negative in all periods. None of these correlations can be taken as evidence of any strong Phillips curve effect.

CHAPTER 3

PRACTICE PROBLEMS

PP 3.4

The null and alternative hypotheses are, H_0: $\beta = 0.1$ and H_1: $\beta \neq 0.1$. The computed t-statistic is t_c = (0.13875-0.1)/0.01873 = 2.069. Under the null hypothesis, this has a student's t-distribution with 12 degrees of freedom. The critical values of t are 2.179 and 3.055 for 5 percent and 1 percent levels of significance respectively. Because the absolute value of t_c is less than these critical values, we cannot reject the hypothesis that $\beta = 0.1$.

PP 3.6

For a one-tailed test (H_0: $\beta = 0$, H_1: $\beta > 0$), the coefficient is insignificant at the 10 percent level if $t_c < t_{12}^*(0.1)$, where t^* is the point on the t-distribution such that the area to the right is 0.1. For a lower significance level (say 5 percent), $t_{12}^*(0.05)$ must be greater than $t_{12}^*(0.1)$. Hence t_c must be less than $t_{12}^*(0.05)$ also, implying that the coefficient is insignificant at the 5 percent level. It is readily seen that this argument applies to any level below 10 percent.

PP 3.7

The original model is PRICE $= \hat{\alpha} + \hat{\beta}$ SQFT. Substituting $1000 + X^*$ for SQFT, we have, PRICE $= \hat{\alpha} + \hat{\beta}\,(1000 + X^*) = \hat{\alpha} + 1000\hat{\beta} + \hat{\beta} X^* = \hat{a} + \hat{b} X^*$. Therefore, $\hat{a} = \hat{\alpha} + 1000\hat{\beta}$ and $\hat{b} = \hat{\beta}$.

PP 3.8

We have $\hat{\alpha}$ = 0.176496, $s_{\hat{\alpha}}$ = 0.467509, $\hat{\beta}$ = 0.141652, $s_{\hat{\beta}}$ = 0.002875, and d.f. = 49. Therefore, for a 95 percent confidence interval, t^* = 2.01. Therefore the confidence intervals are

$$For\,\alpha = 0.176496 \pm (2.01 \times 0.467509) = (-0.763197, 1.1161891)$$

$$For\,\beta = 0.141652 \pm (2.01 \times 0.002875) = (0.1358732, 0.1474307$$

EXERCISES

EX 3.1

Equations (a) and (b) are valid because of the normal Equations (3.4) and (3.5). However, there is no reason why the true errors u_t should satisfy similar conditions *in the sample*.

EX 3.2

The error term is u_t which is Y_t minus $\alpha + \beta X_t$. The residual is the corresponding expression using the sample regression function. That is, it is $\hat{u}_t = Y_t - \hat{\alpha} - \hat{\beta} X_t$. u_t is the true error for the tth observation but $E(u_t)$ is the corresponding population expectation. $E(\hat{u}_t) = E(Y_t - \hat{\alpha} - \hat{\beta} X_t) = E(\alpha + \beta X_t + u_t - \hat{\alpha} - \hat{\beta} X_t)$. Assume that X_t is given and non-random. This means that it can be taken out of expectations. α and β are true parameters and are fixed. Therefore the above expectation is

$$\alpha + \beta X_t + E(u_t) - E(\hat{\alpha}) - E(\hat{\beta} X_t)$$

By the unbiasedness property, $E(\hat{\alpha}) = \alpha$ and $E(\hat{\beta}) = \beta$. Substituting this and assuming that $E(u_t) = 0$, we see that all the terms cancel out and hence the expectation is zero.

EX 3.4

a. To estimate by the OLS procedure all we need are at least two observations and Assumption 3.2 that $S_{xx} > 0$. This is readily seen from Equation (3.10).

b. For properties (3.4) and (3.5) of unbiasedness and consistency we need, in addition to the above assumptions, also that $E(u_t) = 0$ and that X_t is given and non-random. X_t non-random also implies that $\text{Cov}(X_t, u_t) = 0$. See the proofs of these properties in the appendix to Chapter 3.

c. Efficiency is proven by the Gauss-Markov Theorem which also requires the Assumptions 3.5 and 3.6. See the proofs in the appendix to Chapter 3.

d. Hypothesis testing requires that the error terms u_t also have the normal distribution. See the derivation for the t- and F- distributions.

EX 3.5

a. X values being closer to their mean implies that S_{xx} is smaller. From Equations 3.18 and 3.19, we see that a smaller S_{xx} means a larger variance. Thus the estimates are less precisely estimated and the statement is FALSE.

b. FALSE because for unbiasedness we need Assumptions 3.3 and 3.4. Violation of Assumption 3.4 implies that unbiasedness is no longer valid.

c. Assumption 3.8 is needed only for hypothesis testing. Thus BLUE still holds and the statement is FALSE.

d. TRUE because t- and F- distributions for the test statistics were derived from the assumption of normality which is a must for hypothesis testing.

e. TRUE because the width of a confidence interval directly depends on the standard error of an estimate.

f. TRUE because if Var(X) is large, then from equations 3.18 and 3.19 the variances will be smaller and hence confidence intervals will be narrower.

g. FALSE because a high p-value means rejection of H_0 might result in a high probability of Type I error. So we should not reject, implying that we should not conclude that the coefficient is significant.

h. TRUE because a higher level of significance means a lower value for t^* and hence actual $|t_c|$ is more likely to be to the right of t^*. Also, a higher level of significance means a greater chance for p-value to be below it and hence more likely for the null hypothesis to be rejected, implying significance of a coefficient.

i. PARTLY TRUE. Violation of Assumptions 3.5 and 3.6 only affects the BLUE property. Thus estimators are still unbiased and consistent but not BLUE.

j. FALSE. The null hypothesis is a statement about whether or not the parameter has a certain value. This is either true or not true and therefore it is meaningless to attribute a probability to whether H_0 is true or not. However, the rejection of a true hypothesis, which is Type I error, is a random event because it can change from trial to trial. The p-value is the probability of making this type of mistake.

EX 3.7

The scatter diagram for this is given in the next page. The estimate of the slope is now

$$\hat{\beta} = \frac{1}{n} \Sigma \left[\frac{Y_t - \bar{Y}}{X_t - \bar{X}} \right]$$

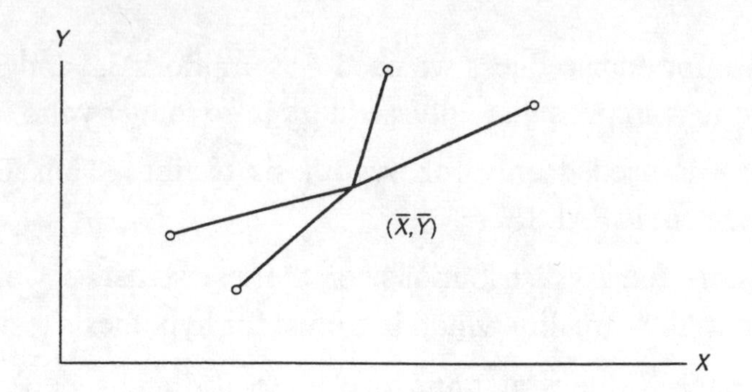

To compute the expected value note that $Y_t - \bar{Y} = \beta(X_t - \bar{X}) + u_t - \bar{u}$. As before, the error terms have expectation zero and hence $E(Y_t - \bar{Y}) = \beta(X_t - \bar{X})$. It readily follows that $\hat{\beta}$ is unbiased. By the Gauss-Markov Theorem, this is inferior to the OLS estimator.

EX 3.8

The slope of the line connecting the first and second point is $(Y_2 - Y_1)/(X_2 - X_1)$. The slope of the line connecting the second and third points is $(Y_3 - Y_2)/(X_3 - X_2)$. By proceeding similarly, the slope of the line connecting point $t-1$ with t is given by $(Y_t - Y_{t-1})/(X_t - X_{t-1})$.

The scatter diagram for this is given below.

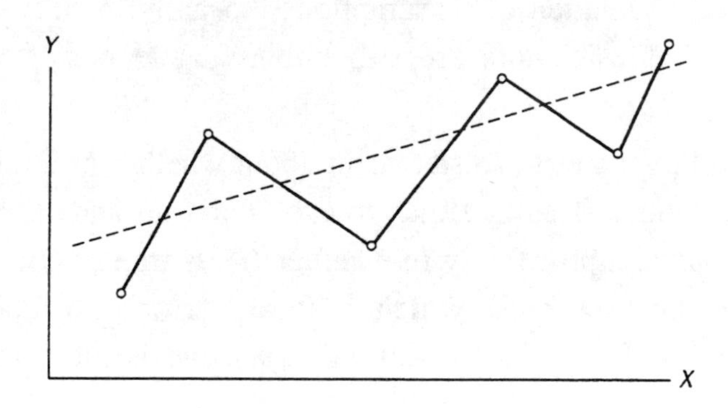

The average of all the slopes in the scatter diagram is given by

$$\tilde{\beta} = \frac{1}{n-1} \sum_{2}^{n} \left[\frac{Y_t - Y_{t-1}}{X_t - X_{t-1}} \right]$$

To compute the expected value of $\tilde{\beta}$, we have,

$$\frac{Y_t - Y_{t-1}}{X_t - X_{t-1}} = \frac{\alpha + \beta X_t + u_t - \alpha - \beta X_{t-1} - u_{t-1}}{X_t - X_{t-1}} = \beta + \frac{u_t - u_{t-1}}{X_t - X_{t-1}}$$

Hence,

$$\tilde{\beta} = \beta + \frac{1}{n-1}\sum_{2}^{n}\left[\frac{u_t - u_{t-1}}{X_t - X_{t-1}}\right]$$

X_t is nonrandom and $E(u_t) = E(u_{t-1}) = 0$. Therefore, $E(\tilde{\beta}) = \beta$, which means that $\tilde{\beta}$ is unbiased. By the Gauss-Markov Theorem, OLS estimates are most efficient among unbiased linear estimators. This implies that any other such estimator, in particular $\tilde{\beta}$, is inefficient (or at least is no more efficient) than the OLS estimate.

EX 3.9

The scatter diagram for this is given below.

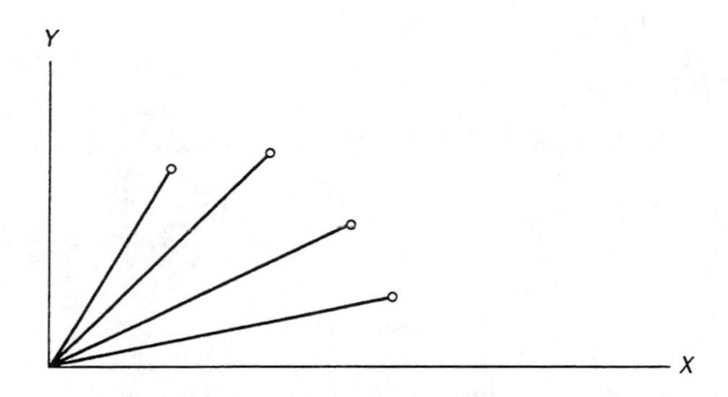

The average of all the slopes in the scatter diagram is given by

$$\tilde{\beta} = \frac{1}{n}\sum_{1}^{n}\left[\frac{Y_t}{X_t}\right]$$

To compute the expected value of $\tilde{\beta}$, we have,

$$\frac{Y_t}{X_t} = \frac{\alpha + \beta X_t + u_t}{X_t} = \beta + \frac{\alpha + u_t}{X_t}$$

Hence,

$$\tilde{\beta} = \beta + \frac{1}{n}\sum_{1}^{n}\left[\frac{\alpha + u_t}{X_t}\right]$$

X_t is nonrandom and $E(u_t) = 0$. Therefore, $E(\tilde{\beta}) = \beta + \frac{1}{n}\Sigma\frac{\alpha}{X_t} \neq \beta$, which means that $\tilde{\beta}$ is biased. We note from the scatter diagram that, intuitively, this is not a very good estimate and one would therefore not try to use it to estimate β.

EX 3.10

From the model, $\bar{Y} = \alpha + \beta\bar{X} + \bar{u}$. Therefore, $\tilde{\beta} = \dfrac{\bar{Y}}{\bar{X}} = \beta + \dfrac{\alpha + \bar{u}}{\bar{X}}$. Taking the expected value and noting, as before, that X is non-random and that $E(\bar{u}) = E(u_t) = 0$, we have, $E(\tilde{\beta}) = \beta + \dfrac{\alpha}{\bar{X}} \neq \beta$. Therefore $\tilde{\beta}$ is biased.

EX 3.11

The term $(Y_t - Y_{t-1})/(X_t - X_{t-1})$ is the slope of the straight line connecting the adjacent points (X_{t-1}, Y_{t-1}) and (X_t, Y_t). Therefore, $\tilde{\beta}$ is the average of the slopes of the straight lines connecting successive data points. See the answers to Exercise 3.3 for the rest of the answers.

EX 3.13

The model is $Y_t = \beta X_t + u_t$.

(a) The slope of the straight line from the origin to (X_t, Y_t) is Y_t/X_t. The average of this for $t = 1, 2, \cdots n$ is $\beta^* = \dfrac{1}{n} \Sigma \left[\dfrac{Y_t}{X_t}\right]$.

(b) $\dfrac{Y_t}{X_t} = \dfrac{\beta X_t + u_t}{X_t} = \beta + \left[\dfrac{u_t}{X_t}\right]$

As before, X_t is nonrandom and $E(u_t) = 0$. Hence $E(Y_t/X_t) = \beta$ and $E(\beta^*) = \beta$. β^* is thus unbiased.

(c) By the Gauss-Markov Theorem, OLS estimator is the most efficient (has the smallest variance among unbiased linear estimators), and hence is superior to β^*.

EX 3.14

The estimated coefficient is $\hat{\beta} = \Sigma X_t Y_t / \Sigma(X_t^2)$. Substitute from the true model to obtain

$$\hat{\beta} = \frac{\Sigma[X_t(\alpha + \beta X_t + u_t)]}{\Sigma X_t^2} = \alpha \frac{\Sigma X_t}{\Sigma X_t^2} + \beta + \frac{\Sigma X_t u_t}{\Sigma X_t^2}$$

The expected value of the third term is zero because $E(u_t) = 0$. But $\hat{\beta}$ will be biased unless the first term is also zero. The required condition is therefore that $\Sigma X_t = 0$ or that the sample mean is zero.

EX 3.15

$Cov(X_t, \hat{u}_t) = E(X_t \hat{u}_t) - X_t E(\hat{u}_t)$. Note that X_t is non-random and hence it can be taken out of the expectation. Also, $\hat{u}_t$ is a linear combination of the u's with zero expectation. It follows that the covariance between X_t and $\hat{u}_t$ is zero.

EX 3.16

Comparing Equations (3.14) with Equation (2.10), we note that $S_{xy} = (n-1)\, Cov(X, Y)$. Similarly, frm Equations (3.13) and (2.9), we see that $S_{xx} = (n-1)\, Var(X)$. Therefore, the estimated slope coefficient can also be written as

$$\hat{\beta} = \frac{Cov(X, Y)}{Var(X)}$$

EX 3.17

From Equation (3.10), $\hat{\beta} = S_{xy}/S_{xx}$, where S_{xx} and S_{xy} are defined as in Equations (3.11) and (3.12). Also, from Equations (2.9) and (2.10), $S_{xx} = (n-1)s_x^2$ and $S_{xy} = (n-1)s_{xy}$. $\hat{\beta}$ can be rewritten as follows:

$$\hat{\beta} = \frac{S_{xy}}{S_{xx}} = \frac{s_{xy}}{s_x^2} = \frac{s_{xy}}{s_x s_y} \cdot \frac{s_y}{s_x} = r\,\frac{s_y}{s_x}$$

because $r = s_{xy}/(s_x s_y)$ from equation (2.11). The estimated relation is $\hat{Y}_t = \hat{\alpha} + \hat{\beta} X_t = \bar{Y} - \hat{\beta}\bar{X} + \hat{\beta} X_t = \bar{Y} + \hat{\beta}\,(X_t - \bar{X})$. Using the expression for $\hat{\beta}$ just derived, we have the desired result.

EX 3.19

The regression model will have the form $S_t = \alpha + \beta\, t + u_t$, where t is time from 1 through 25. The data column for the dependent variable will be just the sales in each of the years and that for t will take the value 1 for the first year, 2 for the second year, and so on. The estimated sales in the 28th year is $\hat{\alpha} + 28\hat{\beta}$.

EX 3.20

To answer this question, examine the expression for R^2 given in Equation (3.23) and ask yourself what happens when Y is a constant for all observations.

EX 3.21

The normal equation for this model is given by $\Sigma X_t \hat{u}_t = \Sigma X_t (Y_t - \hat{\beta} X_t) = 0$. The sum of squares $\Sigma\, Y_t^2$ can be written as

$$\Sigma Y_t^2 = \Sigma(Y_t - \hat{Y}_t + \hat{Y}_t)^2 = \Sigma(\hat{u}_t + \hat{Y}_t)^2 = \Sigma \hat{u}_t^2 + \Sigma \hat{Y}_t^2 + 2\,\Sigma \hat{u}_t\, \hat{Y}_t$$

The third term is zero because

$$\Sigma \hat{u}_t \hat{Y}_t = \Sigma \hat{u}_t \hat{\beta} X_t = \hat{\beta} \Sigma X_t \hat{u}_t = 0$$

by the normal equation just stated. It follows from this that $\Sigma Y_t^2 = \Sigma \hat{Y}_t^2 + \Sigma \hat{u}_t^2$.

EX 3.22

1a. The constant term is an estimate of the expected average life insurance a family has when the family income is zero.

1b. The coefficient on income is the expected average change in life insurance for each one dollar increase in family income.

1c. The value $\hat{\alpha} + \hat{\beta} x_0$ is an estimate of the expected average life insurance when the family income is x_0.

1d. The value of R^2 is a measure of the fraction of the variation in life insurance explained by the model. It is also the square of the correlation coefficient between observed life insurance and the average value predicted by the estimated equation.

2a. The population regression function is $\alpha + \beta$ *income*.

2b. As explained in Section 3.1, the population error terms arise because of omitted variables, nonlinearities, measurement errors, and unpredictable effects.

3a. Unbiasedness of an estimated coefficient means that, although the estimates will differ in repeated trials, the average of those estimates over a large number of trials will be the true population mean. For a regression line, unbiasedness means that the average of the estimated relations from repeated trials will be the population regression function given in 2a.

3b. For unbiasedness, we need Assumption (3.3) that $E(u_t) = 0$ and Assumption (3.4) that the Xs (which are income values in this example) are given and non-random, or that $\mathrm{Cov}(X_t, u_t) = 0$, that is, that income and the error term are uncorrelated.

3c. The assumption that $E(u_t) = 0$ is not likely to hold here because u_t captures the effects of important omitted variables such as the size of the family and the age distribution of any children. These effects are not likely to be zero.

4a. H_0: $\beta = 5$, $H_1 < 5$.

4b. The test statistic is given by

$$t_c = \frac{\hat{\beta} - 5}{s_{\hat{\beta}}} = \frac{5 - 3.880186}{0.112125} = 9.987$$

where $\hat{\beta}$ is the estimate of β and $s_{\hat{\beta}}$ is the estimate of the standard error of $\hat{\beta}$. Because the alternative is one-sided, we use a one-tailed t-test. The d.f. are $n - 2 = 18$ and the 5% critical value is 1.734. Since $t_c > 1.734$, we reject the null hypothesis.

4c. The conclusion is that the observed estimate of β is significantly below 5.

4d. For a 95 confidence interval we need $t^*_{18}(0.025)$ which is 2.101. We have $\hat{\beta} \pm (t^* \times s_{\hat{\beta}}) = 3.880186 \pm (2.101 \times 0.112125) = (3.645, 4.116)$.

5a. Because the maximum likelihood method gives the same answers as the OLS procedure, the methodology is sound.

5b. Yes, as mentioned earlier, important variables such as the size and age distribution of the children should be included as added variables in the model. Also the wealth or asset position of the family would be important because, the higher the wealth of a family the less the need for life insurance.

EX 3.23

a. If income is zero, households typically receive earned income credit which is like a negative income tax. Thus the negative sign for the constant term is sensible. The positive sign for income also agrees with our intuition because, the higher the income the more the income tax.

b. An increase of one billion dollars in total income is expected to increase the tax, on average, by 0.142 billion dollars, that is, by 142 million dollars.

c. For the constant term, the null and alternative hypotheses are H_0: $\alpha = 0$, H_1: $\alpha \neq 0$. Similarly, for β. Because the p-value for the income coefficient is well below 0.05, that coefficient is significantly different from zero. However, the intercept term is not because its p-value is higher than 0.05.

EX 3.26

a. As *Miles* or *Age* increase, we would expect the cost to increase also. The slope coefficients would therefore be expected to be positive, which they are. When *Age* or *Miles* are zero, we would expect cost to be zero also. The constant terms would be expected to be zero. The actual signs are negative and counterintuitive. This indicates possible model misspecification. For instance, suppose the actual relation between Y and X is curvilinear as in the following figure and starts at the origin. But if we fit a straight line to the data, the estimated intercept term might be negative. This example suggests that the sign and magnitude of the estimated constant term might be unimportant.

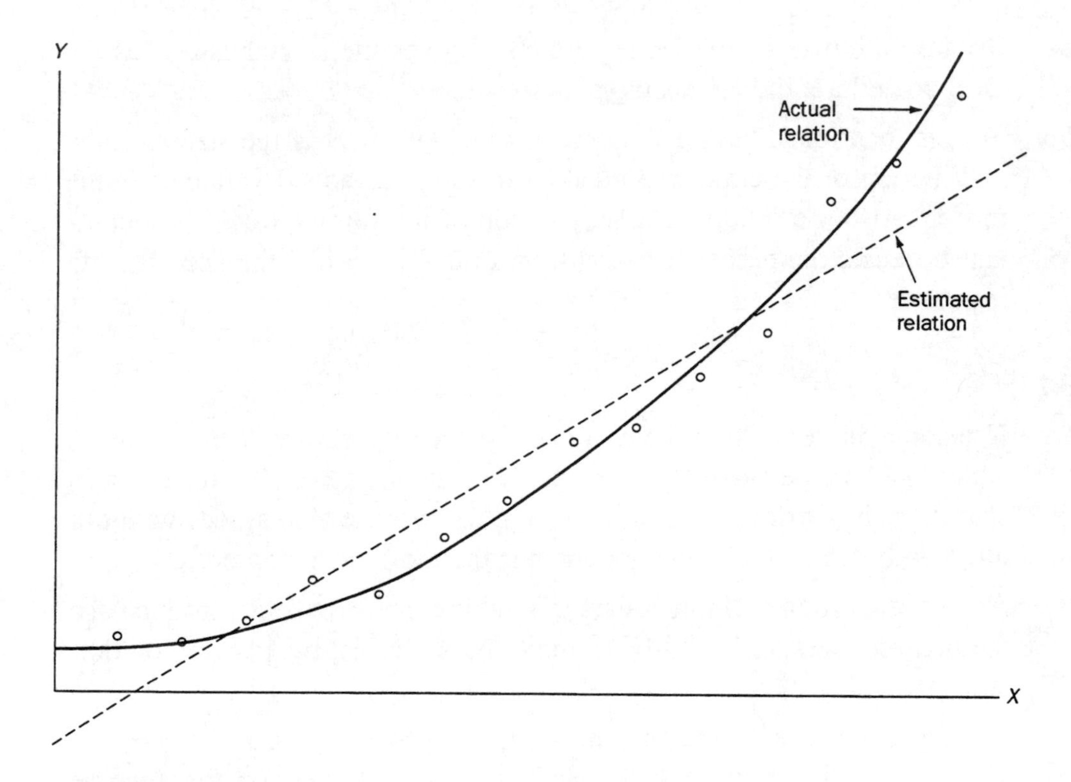

b. Model A fits better because it has a higher value for R^2. Thus the age of the car is a better predictor than the mileage. However, since the gain in R^2 is only 0.042, the improvement in fit is not much.

c. The t-statistics for both $\hat{\alpha}$ and $\hat{\beta}$ are very high and indicate significance. The critical t^* for 55 d.f. is about 3.5 for the 0.1 percent (that is, 0.001) level.

Both t-values are well above this which means that the regression coefficients are statistically very significantly different from zero.

d. If Age^* is the age in days, then $Age^* = 7\ Age$. The new estimated Model A is $cost = -\ 625.935025 + 7.343478\ (1/7)\ Age^* = -\ 625.935025 + 1.049068\ Age^*$. Only the coefficient for Age^* and its standard error (which will now be 0.32958/7 = 0.04708) are affected. R^2, t-, and F-statistics are unchanged.

EX 3.27

a. R^2 of 0.186 indicates that over 80% of the variation in salary gain is unexplained by the tuition charged by the business school. The salary would depend on the quality of the training, the placement, the school's reputation in general, and so on.

b. The null hypothesis is that a particular coefficient is zero and the alternative is that it is different from zero. The test statistics are the coefficients divided by the corresponding standard errors. Under the null hypothesis, they have the t-distribution with d.f. $n - 2 = 23$. The critical value of a 10 percent test is $t^*_{23}(0.05) = 1.714$. The t-statistic for the constant term is 11.101/12.03 = 0.922 and the same for the slope term is 1.433/0.562 = 2.55. Since $t_c < t^*$ for the constant term but $> t^*$ for the slope term, the former is insignificant and latter is significant.

c. Let Tuition* = 1000 Tuition and Gain* = 1000 Gain. Substituting for Tuition and Gain in the model, we get the new estimated model as

$$\text{Gain*} = \underset{(12030)}{11101} + \underset{(0.562)}{1.433}\ \text{Tuition*}$$

The value of R^2 is unchanged.

EX 3.28

a. In Section 3.5 we described how to test the model as a whole with an F-test. The null hypothesis is that X and Y are uncorrelated (that is $\rho_{XY} = 0$) and the alternative is that they are correlated. The test statistic is $F_c = R^2(n-2)/(1-R^2)$. In our example, $n = 427$ and the F-statistics for the three models are, respectively, 84, 32, and 60. For a 1 percent-level of significance, the critical $F^*_{1,425}(0.01)$ is approximately 6.7. Because the calculated F-values are well above this, we reject the null hypothesis of lack of correlation between X and Y and conclude that they are correlated. This means that all three models are significant overall.

b. The null hypothesis is that a particular regression coefficient is zero. The alternative for a two-tailed test is that it is nonzero. The critical t^*_{425} (0.0025) is slightly above 2.807. If an observed t-value exceeds this (in absolute terms) we reject the null hypothesis and conclude that the coefficient is statistically significant. The calculated t-values are:

$$
\begin{aligned}
0.92058/0.20463 &= 4.50 \\
0.52417/0.05712 &= 9.18 \\
1.99740/0.14128 &= 14.14 \\
0.00157/0.00028 &= 5.61 \\
1.62845/0.15135 &= 10.76 \\
0.00204/0.00026 &= 7.85
\end{aligned}
$$

Because all the t-statistics exceed the critical value, every regression coefficient in every model is statistically significantly different from zero.

c. The low values for R^2 indicate that the independent variables HSGPA, VSAT, and MSAT do not explain much of the variance in COLGPA. We will see in later chapters that a more extended model does better.

EX 3.30

The estimated model is given below:

VARIABLE	COEFFICIENT	STDERROR	T STAT	2Prob(t > |T|)
constant	11.808703	0.912085	12.94693	< 0.0001 ***
assets	-0.028368	0.01039	-2.730253	0.009734 ***

```
Error Sum of Sq (ESS) 873.415312    Std Err of Resid. (sgmahat)   4.9256
R-squared                   0.172
F-statistic (1, 36)         7.454281   pvalue = Prob(F > 7.454) is 0.009734
```

The degrees of freedom are 38-2 = 36 and the critical value for 10 percent (two-tailed) is t^*_{36} (0.05), which is in the range (1.684, 1.697). We note that the regression coefficients for both variables have t-statistics above this in numerical values, indicating statistical significance. This is confirmed by the p-values which are well below 0.10. The overall significance is tested by the F-test. The test statistic is 7.454281 with the p-value 0.009734 and hence we reject the null hypothesis that the coefficient of correlation between assets and returns is zero. Although this appears to indicate a good overall fit, the value of R^2 is only 0.172. Thus, less than 20 percent of the variance in returns is explained by the assets of a company. Rates of return would depend on other factors such as the the wage rate, interest rate, cost of materials and other inputs.

EX 3.31

a. The estimated model is given below.

VARIABLE	COEFFICIENT	STDERROR	T STAT	2Prob(t > |T|)
constant	83.575294	118.130922	0.70748	0.485812
SALES	18.433756	4.446325	4.145841	0.00034 ***

```
Error Sum of Sq (ESS) 3.4685e+06   Std Err of Resid. (sgmahat) 372.478
R-squared                0.407
F-statistic (1, 25)   17.187994    pvalue = Prob(F > 17.188) is 0.00034
```

b. The scatter diagram is given below.

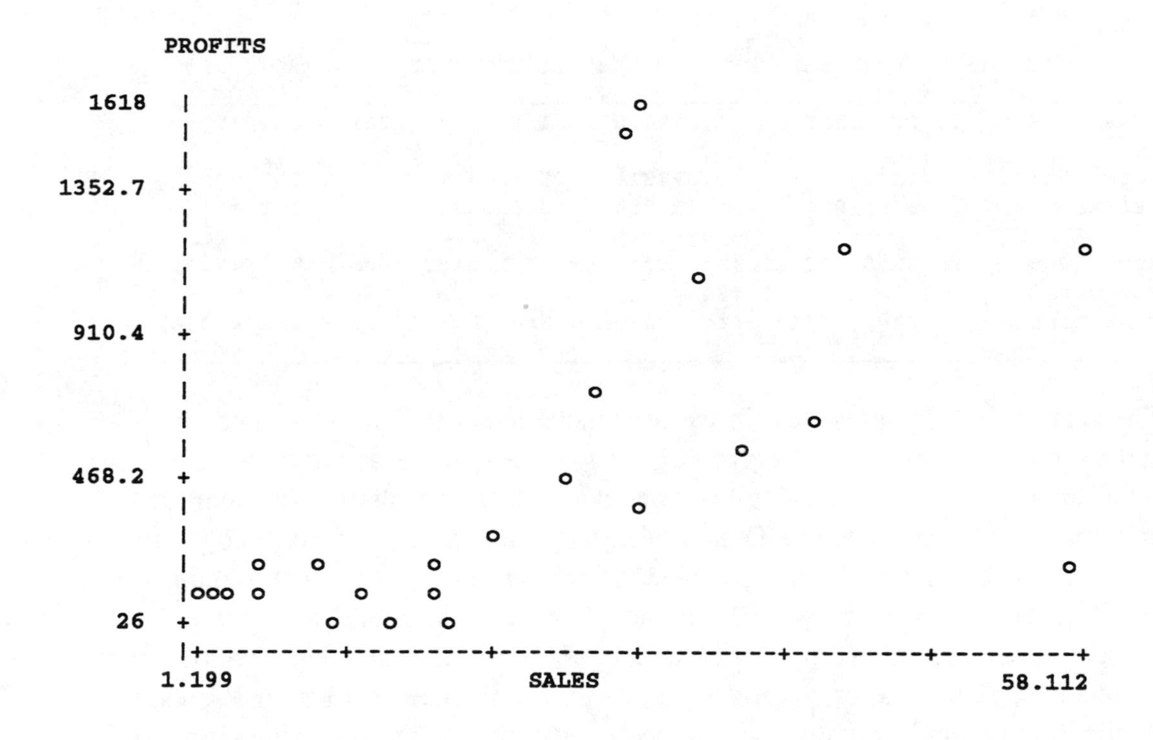

c. The standard error of residuals and the standard errors of individual coefficients are presented in the table, as are the t-statistics and the corresponding p-values.

d. The null hypothesis is that the coefficient is zero and the alternative is that it is not zero. The p-value for SALES is quite low indicating strong significance. For the constant term, however, the p-value is almost 50 percent. Thus, if we reject the null hypothesis that $\alpha = 0$, we are likely to make the Type I error approximately 48.6 percent of the time. As this probability is unacceptably high, we should not reject the null hypothesis but instead conclude that the constant term is not significant.

e. Let PROFIT* be profits in dollars. Then PROFITS* = 1000000 PROFITS*. Substituting this in the model, we get PROFIT* = 83,575,294 + 18,433,756 SALES. Thus both regression coefficients are multiplied by a million. The standard errors will also be multiplied by it and the error sum of squared will be multiplied by a million squared. However, R^2, t-, and F-statistics are independent of units and will be unchanged.

EX 3.32

The estimated coefficients and associated statistics are given below.

VARIABLE	COEFFICIENT	STDERROR	T STAT	2Prob(t > |T|)
constant	52.237497	2.372816	22.014979	< 0.0001 ***
YEARS	1.491101	0.113559	13.130596	< 0.0001 ***

```
Error Sum of Sq (ESS) 70611.387   Std Err of Resid. (sgmahat)  17.915
R-squared                 0.439
F-statistic (1, 220)     172.41   pvalue = Prob(F > 172.413) is < 0.01
```

The scatter diagram presented in the next page does not indicate a good fit. The test for overall significance is given by the F-statistic in the above table. Because it has an extremely low p-value, we conclude that the correlation between salary and number of years since Ph.D. is significantly different from zero. The p-values for both the constant and the coefficient for years are below 0.0001 indicating significance at levels below 0.01 percent. However, the model explains only 44 percent of the variation in salaries and is hence inadequate. Number of years since Ph.D. is not the only variable that would influence salaries. A Professor's publication record, reputation among peers, visibility in the profession, and so on, are very important and hence measures of these characteristics should be included in the model.

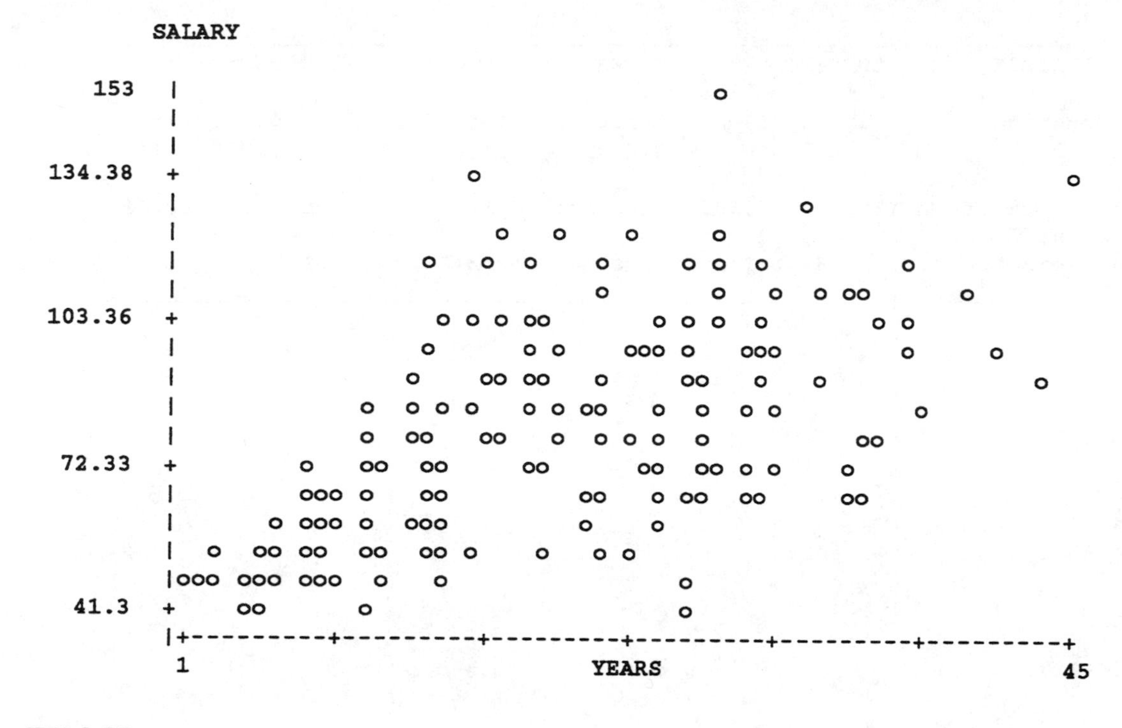

EX 3.33

The ESL commands for this exercise are reproduced below.

```
genr time
graph pop year ;
smpl 1962 1989
ols pop const time ;
fcast 1990 1994 pophat
smpl 1990 1994
genr error = pop - pophat
genr abspcerr=100*abs(error)/pop
print -o pop pophat error abspcerr ;
```

Estimated time trend and associated statistics (using the data for 1962-1989) are presented in the next page along with the plot of the U.K. population over time. From the graph we see that a linear trend is not quite appropriate. A polynomial relation might be better (Chapter 6 discusses that model). However, the value of R^2 is 0.84 indicating that time explains 84 percent of the variation in U.K. population. The p-value for the F-statistic is extremely small and hence the overall fit is quite good.

```
VARIABLE          COEFFICIENT      STDERROR      T STAT        2Prob(t > |T|)

constant            54.154373      0.164674   328.859027       < 0.0001 ***
time                  0.11656      0.009921    11.748661       < 0.0001 ***

Error Sum of Sq (ESS) 4.675605    Std Err of Resid. (sgmahat)    0.424065
R-squared                0.841
F-statistic (1, 26) 138.031034    pvalue = Prob(F > 138.031) is < 0.0001
```

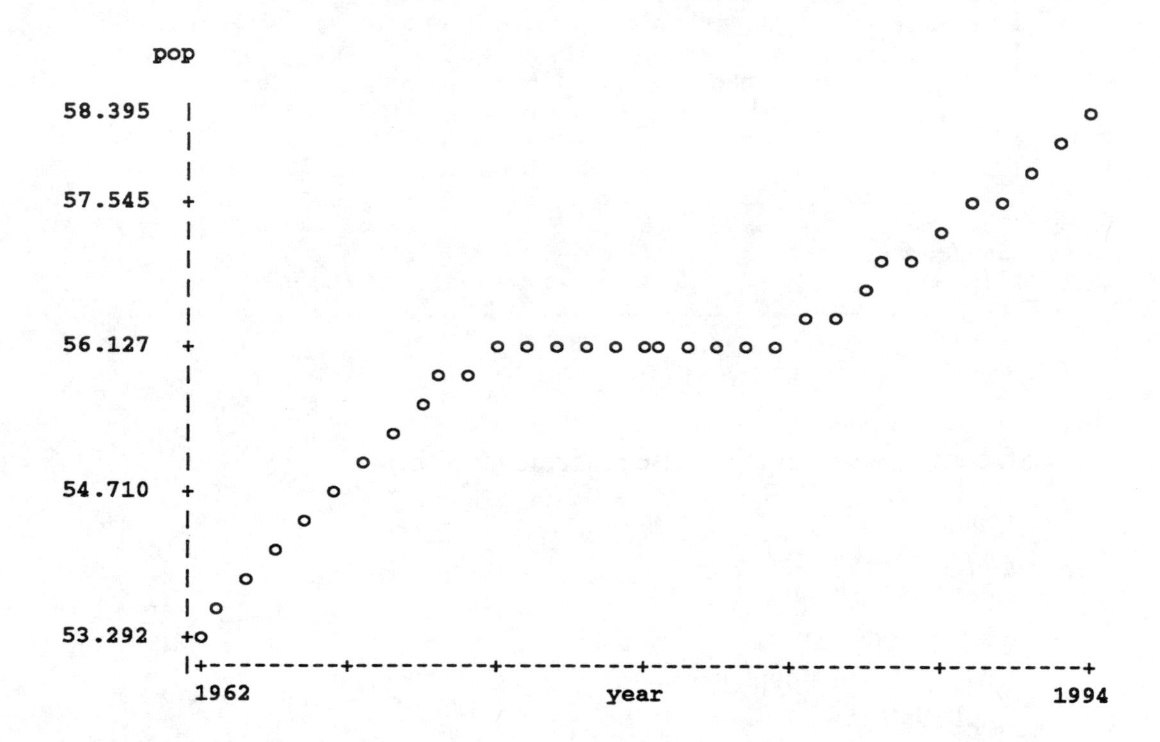

Both the intercept and slope terms are significant at levels below 0.01 percent. Population has been growing at an average annual rate of 0.11656 million but, as is seen from the graph, during 1973 through 1983 population growth was practically nil. The model was projected for the years 1990 through 1994 and the absolute percent error (abspcerr) computed. The values are presented in the next page. It is surprising that the percentage errors are low even though the graph indicated that a linear relation is not a good approximation to the time trend.

Year	pop	pophat	error	abspcerr
1990	57.561	57.534627	0.02637302	0.04581751
1991	57.808	57.651187	0.15681253	0.27126442
1992	58.006	57.767748	0.23825205	0.41073691
1993	58.191	57.884308	0.30669157	0.52704296
1994	58.395	58.000869	0.39413109	0.67493979

EX 3.34

The ESL commands for this exercise are reproduced below.

```
genr time
graph pop year ;
smpl 1948 1989
ols pop const time ;
fcast 1990 1995 pophat
smpl 1990 1995
genr error = pop - pophat
genr abspcerr=100*abs(error)/pop
print -o pop pophat error abspcerr ;
```

The estimated coefficients are presented below along with associated summary statistics using the data for the period 1948 through 1989. The plot of the U.S. population over time is presented in the next page.

VARIABLE	COEFFICIENT	STDERROR	T STAT	2Prob(t > |T|)
constant	147.532146	0.587533	251.104333	< 0.0001 ***
time	2.432977	0.023805	102.205329	< 0.0001 ***

```
Error Sum of Sq (ESS) 139.865   Std Err of Resid. (sgmahat)    1.870
R-squared               0.996
F-statistic (1, 40) 10445.929   pvalue = Prob(F > 10445.929) is < 0.0001
```

As shown in the plot, the time trend tracks U.S. population extremely well. Time explains 99.6 of the variation in U.S. population. The p-values for each of the regression coefficients and for the F-statistic are very low and hence the model fits the data extremely well. On average, U.S. population has been growing at the rate of 2.432977 million per year. The model was projected for the years 1990 through 1995 and the absolute percent error (abspcerr) computed. The values are presented below. They indicate that absolute percentage errors of forecast for 1990-1995 are much lower than those for U.K. and are all below 1 percent.

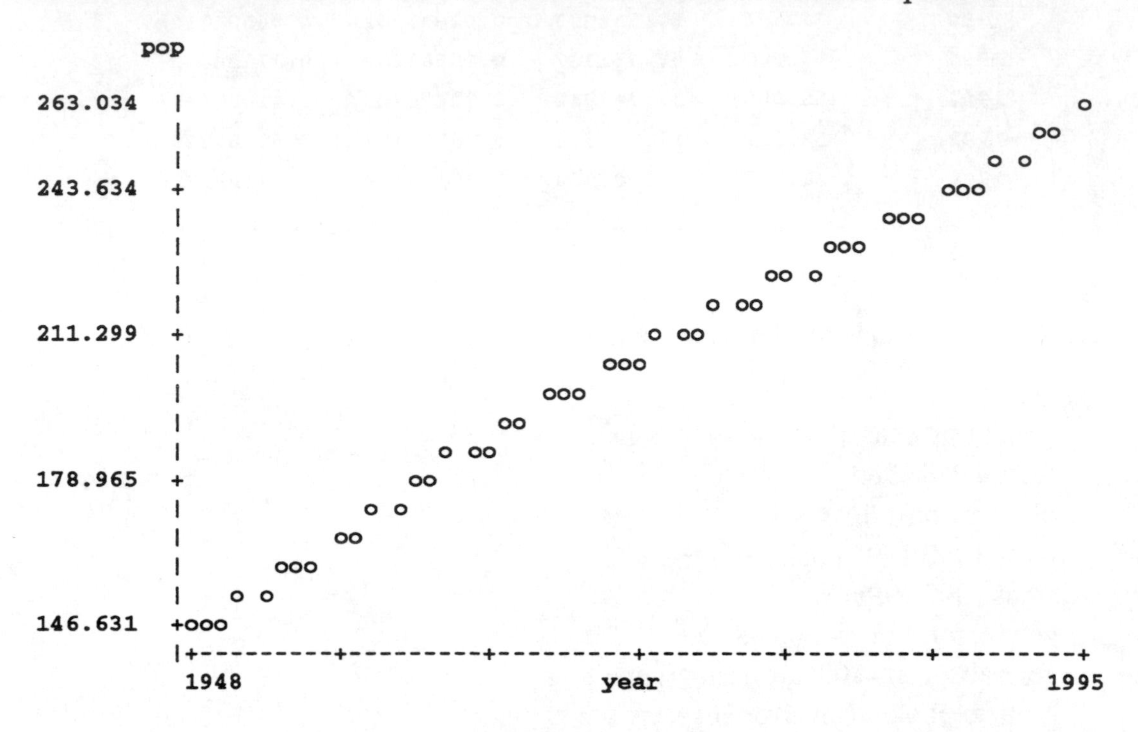

Year	pop	pophat	error	abspcerr
1990	249.913	252.150139	-2.237139	0.89516727
1991	252.65	254.583116	-1.933116	0.76513594
1992	255.419	257.016093	-1.597093	0.62528337
1993	258.137	259.449069	-1.312069	0.50828402
1994	260.66	261.882046	-1.222046	0.46882748
1995	263.034	264.315022	-1.281022	0.48701776

EX 3.35

The estimated relation is presented below and the graph is on the next page.

VARIABLE	COEFFICIENT	STDERROR	T STAT	2Prob(t > |T|)
constant	0.49812	0.535515	0.93017	0.356843
income	0.055573	0.003293	16.875576	< 0.0001 ***

```
Error Sum of Sq (ESS)   417.110     Std Err of Resid. (sgmahat)   2.918
R-squared                 0.853
F-statistic (1, 49)     284.78505  pvalue = Prob(F > 284.785) is < 0.0001
```

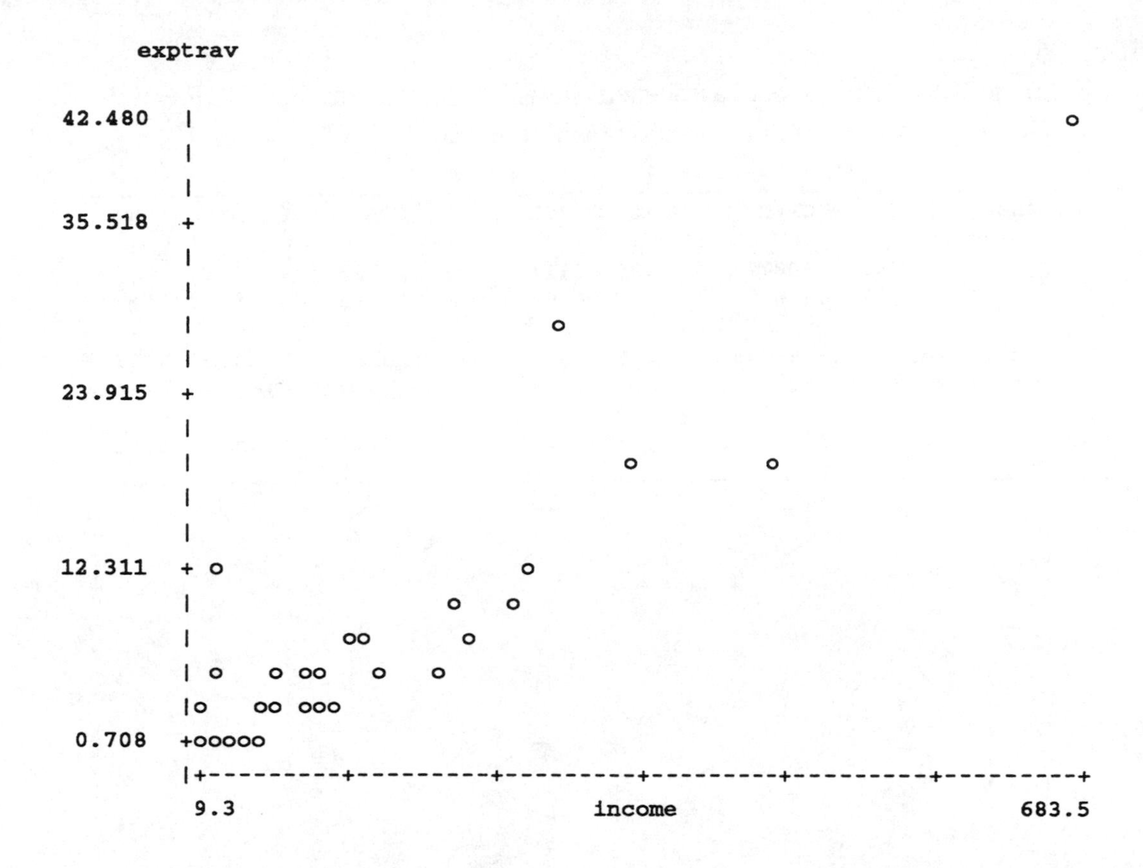

The simple linear regression model explains 85.3 percent of the variation in the expenditure on travel, which is quite good for a cross section study. The overall goodness of fit test has an F-statistic of 284.785 which is extremely significant. The intercept term has a p-value of 0.36 which means that it is not significant even at the 25 percent level. The slope term, however, is highly significant. An increase of one billion dollar in income is expected to increase the average expenditure on travel by 0.055573 billions of dollars or by 55.573 millions of dollars. The graph, however, shows several points away from a regression line. This suggests that there are some missing variables. The size of the population of a state might be an important determinant of the expenditures. Also important are factors such as whether or not the state has milder weather patterns (as in California and Florida) and whether adequate air travel facilities are available in the state. Winter travel is quite difficult in the Northern States and would affect total expenditures.

EX 3.36

Estimated coefficients and associated statistics for the model GDP $= \alpha + \beta$ POP $+ u$ are presented below along with the graph of GDP.

VARIABLE	COEFFICIENT	STDERROR	T STAT	2Prob(t > |T|
constant	-7827.190879	199.421375	-39.249508	< 0.0001 ***
pop	55.091679	0.902972	61.011485	< 0.0001 ***

Mean of dep. var.	4269.528	S.D. of dep. variable	1330.370323
Error Sum of Sq (ESS)	5.607e+05	Std Err of Resid. (sgmahat)	128.416426
R-squared	0.991		
F-statistic (1, 34)	3722.401321	pvalue = Prob(F > 3722.401) is < 0.0001	

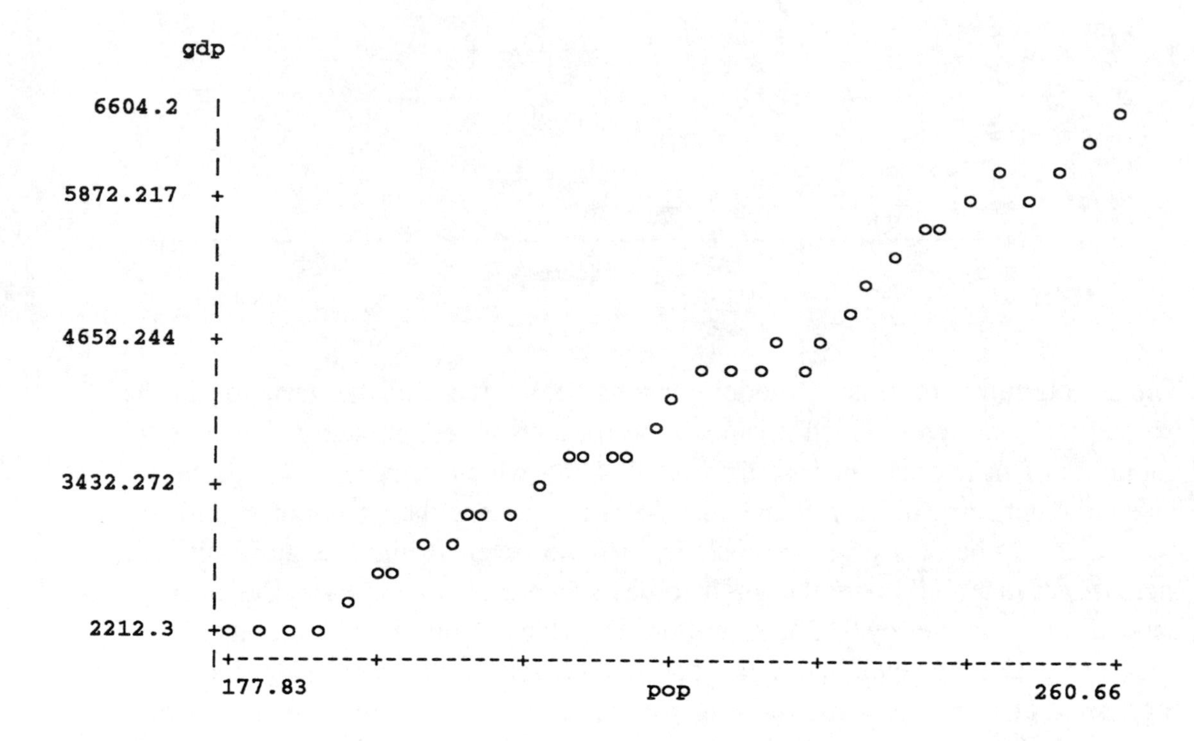

Even though R^2 is 0.991 which is extremely significant with a very high F-statistic, the graph indicates that a linear model is not adequate especially in the early years. Both the intercept and slope terms are significant at levels below 0.01 percent. The estimated coefficients and associated statistics for a model in which a time trend is fitted are presented below.

```
VARIABLE          COEFFICIENT        STDERROR        T STAT    2Prob(t > |T|)

  constant        1942.655873        40.697162     47.734431      < 0.0001 ***
  time             125.77686          1.918127     65.572733      < 0.0001 ***

Mean of dep. var.   4269.528     S.D. of dep. variable          1330.370323
Error Sum of Sq (ESS) 4.86e+05    Std Err of Resid. (sgmahat)    119.5564
R-squared                 0.992
F-statistic (1, 34) 4299.783     pvalue = Prob(F > 4299.783) is < 0.0001
```

The time trend model explains a slightly larger fraction of the variation in GDP (R^2 is 0.992) but the difference is trivial. On average, GDP increased at the rate of 125.77686 billions of dollars.

Let GDP2 be GDP in millions. Then, GDP2 = 1000 GDP. Therefore all the regression coefficients and standard errors will be multiplied by 1000 and the error sum of squares will be multiplied by a million. However, R^2, F- and t-statistics will be unchanged.

CHAPTER 4

PRACTICE PROBLEMS

PP 4.1

The change in expected average price is given by

$$\Delta \widehat{PRICE} = \hat{\beta}_2 \, \Delta SQFT + \hat{\beta}_3 \, \Delta BEDRMS + \hat{\beta}_4 \, \Delta BATHS$$

$$= (0.1548 \times 350) - 21.588 - 12.193 = 20.399$$

The increase in price is thus \$20,399, which appears reasonable.

PP 4.2

The forecast (in thousands of dollars) is 129.062 + (0.1548 × 2500) − (21.588 × 4) − (12.193 × 3) = 393.131, which appears reasonable.

PP 4.3

$$\bar{R}^2 = 1 - \frac{ESS(n-1)}{TSS\,(n-k)} = 1 - \frac{\hat{\sigma}^2(n-1)}{TSS}$$

We readily see that $\bar{R}^2$ and $\hat{\sigma}^2$ move inversely to each other.

PP 4.4

See Practice Computer Session 4.1.

PP 4.5

The F-statistic with Model C as the unrestricted model and Model D as the restricted model is given by

$$F_c = \frac{(ESS_D - ESS_C)/3}{ESS_C/10} = \frac{(101815 - 16700)/3}{1670}$$

which is 16.989, the same value reported in Table 4.2 for Model C. The calculations for Models A and B are similar. For Model D, the error sum of squares (ESS) is $\Sigma(Y_t - \hat{\beta}_1)^2 = \Sigma(Y_t - \bar{Y})^2$, which is the same as the total sum of squares (*TSS*). Therefore $R^2 = 1 - (ESS/TSS) = 0$. It is easy to see that $\bar{R}^2$ is also zero.

PP 4.6

Solving the first restriction for β_3, we have $\beta_3 = 1 - \beta_2$. Substituting this in Equation (4.5), we get $Y_t = \beta_1 + \beta_2 X_{t2} + (1 - \beta_2)X_{t3} + u_t = \beta_1 + X_{t3} + \beta_2(X_{t2} - X_{t3}) + u_t$. Bringing the X_{t3} term, which has no regression coefficient, to the left we obtain the restricted model as

$$Y_t - X_{t3} = \beta_1 + \beta_2(X_{t2} - X_{t3}) + u_t$$

From the second restriction, we have $\beta_3 = -\beta_2$. Substituting this in the unrestricted model and regrouping terms, we get the restricted model

$$Y_t = \beta_1 + \beta_2(X_{t2} - X_{t3}) + u_t$$

PP 4.8

In Practice Computer Session 4.3 add the command *ols housing 0 gnp intrate unemp ;*. It will be seen that this model is inferior to Model A in Example 4.11 in terms of all the model selection criteria. Also, the *t*-statistic for *unemp* is quite low indicating that it is very insignificant.

EXERCISES

EX 4.1

If $\beta_2 = 1$, the model becomes $Y_t = \beta_1 + X_{t2} + \beta_3 X_{t3} + u_t$. Bringing X_{t2}, which has no unknown coefficient, to the left-hand side, we have $Y_t - X_{t2} = \beta_1 + \beta_3 X_{t3} + u_t$. Generate the new variable $Z_t = Y_t - X_{t2}$ and regress Z_t against a constant and X_{t3} to obtain estimates for β_1 and β_3.

EX 4.2

This statement is correct. Suppose there are *m* linear combinations to test. To obtain the restricted model, we would solve each restriction for one of the parameters (different each time) and substitute in the original model. This would mean *m* fewer parameters in the restricted model. The difference in the d.f. between the restricted and unrestricted model would therefore be also *m*.

EX 4.3

Method 1 (Wald test): To impose the restriction, we solve for β_3 as $-\beta_2$. The restricted model is $Y_t = \beta_1 + \beta_2 X_{t1} - \beta_2 X_{t2} + u_t = \beta_1 + \beta_2 (X_{t1} - X_{t2}) + u_t$. To estimate this, we generate $Z_t = X_{t1} - X_{t2}$ and regress Y_t against a constant and Z_t.

The test statistic is the F-statistic (denoted by F_c) given in Equation (4.3). It has one d.f. for the numerator and $n-3$ d.f. for the denominator. Reject the null hypothesis that $\beta_2 + \beta_3 = 0$ against the alternative that it is not zero if $F_c > F^*$, the point on $F_{1,n-3}$ with an area to the right equal to the level of significance. Alternatively, compute $P(F > F_c)$ and reject H_0 if the probability is less than the level of significance.

Method 2 (indirect t-test): Define $\delta = \beta_2 + \beta_3$. Next solve for β_3 as $\delta - \beta_2$. Substituting this in the original model, we get $Y_t = \beta_1 + \beta_2 X_{t1} + \delta X_{t2} - \beta_2 X_{t2} + u_t$ $= \beta_1 + \beta_2 (X_{t1} - X_{t2}) + \delta X_{t3} + u_t$. To estimate this, we generate $Z_t = X_{t1} - X_{t2}$ and regress Y_t against a constant, Z_t, and X_{t3}. The test statistic is the t-statistic (denoted by t_c) corresponding to $\hat{\delta}$. This has the t-distribution with $n-3$ d.f. Reject the null hypothesis that $\beta_2 + \beta_3 = 0$ against the alternative that it is not zero if $t_c > t^*$, the point on t_{n-3} with an area to the right equal to half the level of significance. Alternatively, compute p-value $= 2\,P(t > t_c)$ and reject H_0 if the p-value is less than the level of significance.

Method 3 (direct t-test): The test statistic is the t-statistic given by

$$t_c = \frac{\hat{\beta}_2 + \hat{\beta}_3}{[\hat{Var}(\hat{\beta}_2) + \hat{Var}(\hat{\beta}_3) + 2\,\hat{Cov}(\hat{\beta}_2, \hat{\beta}_3)]^{1/2}}$$

This too has the t-distribution with $n-3$ d.f. Reject the null hypothesis that $\beta_2 + \beta_3 = 0$ against the alternative that it is not zero if $t_c > t^*$, the point on t_{n-3} with an area to the right equal to half the level of significance. Alternatively, compute p-value $= 2\ P(t > t_c)$ and reject H_0 if the p-value is less than the level of significance.

EX 4.4

Method 1 (Wald test): To impose the restriction, we solve for β_3 as $-1 - \beta_2$. The restricted model is $Y_t = \beta_1 + \beta_2 X_{t1} - X_{t2} - \beta_2 X_{t2} + u_t$. Bringing the term X_{t2} that has no unknown coefficient to the left, we obtain the restricted model as $Y_t + X_{t2} = \beta_1 + \beta_2 (X_{t1} - X_{t2}) + u_t$. To estimate this, we generate $Y_t^* = Y_t + X_{t2}$, $Z_t = X_{t1} - X_{t2}$, and regress Y_t^* against a constant and Z_t. The test statistic is the F-statistic (denoted by F_c) given in Equation (4.3). It has one d.f. for the numerator and $n-3$ d.f. for the denominator. Reject the null hypothesis that $\beta_2 + \beta_3 + 1 = 0$ against the alternative that it is not zero if $F_c > F^*$, the point on $F_{1,n-k}$ with an area to the right equal to the level of significance. Alternatively, compute $P(F > F_c)$ and reject H_0 if the probability is less than the level of significance.

Method 2 (indirect t-test): Define $\delta = \beta_2 + \beta_3 + 1$. Next solve for β_3 as $\delta - 1 - \beta_2$. Substituting this in the original model and bringing the X_2 term to the left, we get $Y_t + X_{t2} = \beta_1 + \beta_2 X_{t1} + \delta X_{t2} - \beta_2 X_{t2} + u_t = \beta_1 + \beta_2 (X_{t1} - X_{t2}) + \delta X_{t2} + u_t$. The test statistic is the t-statistic (denoted by t_c) corresponding to $\hat{\delta}$. This has the t-distribution with $n - 3$ d.f. Reject the null hypothesis that $\beta_2 + \beta_3 + 1 = 0$ against the alternative that it is not zero if $t_c > t^*$, the point on t_{n-k} with an area to the right equal to half the level of significance. Alternatively, compute p-value $= 2\,P(t > t_c)$ and reject H_0 if the p-value is less than the level of significance.

Method 3 (direct t-test): The test statistic is the t-statistic given by

$$t_c = \frac{\hat{\beta}_2 + \hat{\beta}_3 + 1}{[\hat{Var}(\hat{\beta}_2) + \hat{Var}(\hat{\beta}_3) + 2\,\hat{Cov}(\hat{\beta}_2, \hat{\beta}_3)]^{1/2}}$$

This too has the t-distribution with $n - 3$ d.f. Reject the null hypothesis that $\beta_2 + \beta_3 + 1 = 0$ against the alternative that it is not zero if $t_c > t^*$, the point on t_{n-3} with an area to the right equal to half the level of significance. Alternatively, compute p-value $= 2\,P(t > t_c)$ and reject H_0 if the probability is less than the level of significance.

EX 4.5

True model: $Y_t = \beta X_t + u_t$

Estimated model: $Y_t = \alpha + \beta X_t + u_t$

OLS estimator of β, using the wrong model, is given by Equation (3.10) as $\hat{\beta} = S_{xy}/S_{xx}$ where S_{xx} and S_{xy} are defined in (3.11) and (3.12). $E(\hat{\beta}) = E(S_{xy})\,/\,S_{xx}$, because X is nonrandom.

$$S_{xy} = \Sigma(Y_t - \bar{Y})(X_t - \bar{X}) = \Sigma(\beta X_t + u_t - \beta\bar{X} - \bar{u})(X_t - \bar{X})$$
$$= \beta\Sigma(X_t - \bar{X})^2 + \Sigma(u_t - \bar{u})(X_t - \bar{X}) = \beta S_{xx} + S_{xu}$$

using similar notation. $E(S_{xy}) = \beta S_{xx} + E(S_{xu}) = \beta S_{xx}$ because $E(u) = 0$. Hence, $E(\hat{\beta}) = \beta$, which implies that $\hat{\beta}$ is unbiased. Thus, adding an irrelevant constant term does not bias the remaining coefficients.

EX 4.7

a. If the density of population goes up, the state is crowded and hence crime might go up also. We expect a positive coefficient for D but it is negative. Increase in non-white population who are typically living in poverty or with low incomes might lead to more crime also. The sign is the expected positive. If income rises, one would think that crime would go down, that is, a negative coefficient, but the actual coefficient is positive. One might argue that if income is higher, then the neighborhood is a target for criminals and hence crime might go up. While this is true of a neighborhood within a city, that is not likely to be the case for the state as a whole. Unemployment rising might lead to more crimes also, but the coefficient is negative which is unexpected. Increasing the number of cops is likely to reduce crime, but the actual effect is positive. The argument that more crime means more cops and hence we would expect a positive sign is wrong because then the causation goes the other way. Essentially, there are two equations, one relating crime to cops and another relating cops to crime. The sign will be positive in the second and negative in the first. Crime often is committed by younger people and so we would expect positive coefficients for both age measures, but AGE1 has the wrong sign. Thus there are several observed coefficients with the wrong signs indicating that there may be model misspecification. In some cases, there may be opposing effects which might cancel out making coefficients insignificant as we observe here.

b. From the t-table, look up t^* for $n - k = 50 - 8 = 42$ degrees of freedom for two-tailed 5% test. It is between 2.000 and 2.021. Any coefficient with a t-value numerically larger than these numbers is significantly different from zero. The actual t-statistics are

D	$-0.0009/0.0006 = -1.5$	NW	$0.0094/0.0104 = 0.90$
Y	$0.0003/0.0001 = 3$	U	$-0.099/0.084 = 1.179$
COP	$1.519/0.276 = 5.5$	AGE1	$-0.0068/0.00034 = -20$
AGE2	$0.0077/0.0038 = 2.026$		

The coefficients for Y, COP, AGE1, and AGE2 are numerically (that is, ignoring the sign) larger than 2.021 and therefore are significant. Those for D, NW, and U are not significant.

c. The variables D, NW, and U are not in Model R. This implies that here the null hypothesis is that the coefficients for these variables is zero. The alternative hypothesis is that at least one of the coefficients is not zero. The test statistic is given by the formula in Equation 4.3.

$$F_c = \frac{(ESSR - ESSU) \times DFU}{ESSU \times (DFR - DFU)} = \frac{(36.85 - 33.41) \times (50 - 8)}{33.41 \times 3} = 1.44$$

Under the null hypothesis this has an F-distribution with d.f. 3 and 42. $F^*(3,42)$ for 5% is between 2.76 and 2.84. Since F_c is below this, we cannot reject the null hypothesis and conclude that the omitted variables indeed have statistically insignificant coefficients.

d. The null hypothesis is that the coefficients for Y, COP, AGE1, and AGE2 are all zero. The F-statistic has the F-distribution with d.f. $k-1 = 4$ for the numerator and $n-k = 50 - 5 = 45$ for the denominator. The p-value of 0.003 means that if we reject the null hypothesis the probability of type I error is very small. Therefore it is safe to reject the null hypothesis and conclude that at least one of the coefficients is not zero.

EX 4.8

a. H_0 is that the coefficients for HSGPA, VSAT, and MSAT are all zero. H_1 is that at least one of the coefficients is nonzero. The test statistic is given in Equation (4.4) as

$$F_c = \frac{0.22/3}{0.78/423} = 39.8$$

Under the null hypothesis this has an F-distribution with d.f. 3 and 423. The critical $F^*(0.01) = 3.8$ which is well below F_c. Therefore we reject the null hypothesis and conclude that at least one of the regression coefficients is nonzero.

b. A single regression coefficient is tested with a t-test. The critical t is $t^*(0.01) = 2.33$ (note that the alternative is one sided). The t-statistics for the coefficients of constant, HSGPA, VSAT, and MSAT are obtained by dividing the corresponding regression coefficients by their standard errors. These values are 1.92, 6.52, 2.63, and 3.46. Except for the constant term, all the rest are above 2.33. Therefore we conclude that all the coefficients are significant at the one percent level with the exception of the constant term which is not significant.

c. $\Delta \widehat{\text{COLGPA}} = 0.0007375\ \Delta\ \text{VSAT} + 0.001015\ \ \Delta\,\text{MSAT} = 0.073754 + 0.1015 = 0.175254$

The expected average increase in COLGPA is therefore 0.175.

d. Let the general unrestricted model (U) be

$$\text{COLGPA} = \beta_1 + \beta_2\ \text{HSGPA} + \beta_3\ \text{VSAT} + \beta_4\ \text{MSAT} + u$$

The marginal effect of VSAT is β_3 and the marginal effect of MSAT is β_4. The test is therefore $\beta_3 = \beta_4$. The alternative is that these two coefficients are unequal.

Method 1 (the Wald test): Assume this condition and obtain the restricted model (R) as

$$\text{COLGPA} = \beta_1 + \beta_2\ \text{HSGPA} + \beta_3\ (\text{VSAT} + \text{MSAT}) + v$$

Generate the new variable Z = VSAT + MSAT. Next regress COLGPA against a constant, HSGPA, and Z, and save the error sum of squares. The Wald F-statistic is given by Equation (4.3). Reject H_0: $\beta_3 = \beta_4$ if $F_c > F^*$, where F^* is obtained from $F(1,423)$ such that the area to the right is equal to the level of significance.

Method 2 (an indirect t-test): Let $\beta = \beta_3 - \beta_4$. Solving for β_4, we get $\beta_4 = \beta_3 - \beta$. Substitute this in Model U. The modified model is

$$\text{COLGPA} = \beta_1 + \beta_2\ \text{HSGPA} + \beta_3\ \text{VSAT} + (\beta_3 - \beta)\ \text{MSAT} + u$$

Combining the β_3 terms together, we get

$$\text{COLGPA} = \beta_1 + \beta_2\ \text{HSGPA} + \beta_3\ \text{Z} - \beta\ \text{MSAT} + u$$

where Z has been defined before. The test is conducted by regressing COLGPA against a constant, HSGPA, Z, and MSAT, and using the regular t-test on the coefficient of MSAT.

Method 3 (direct t-test): The variance of the estimated difference $\hat{\beta}_3 - \hat{\beta}_4$ is given by $\text{Var}\ (\hat{\beta}_3) + \text{Var}\ (\hat{\beta}_4) - 2\ \text{Cov}\ (\hat{\beta}_3, \hat{\beta}_4)$. The computed t-statistic is therefore

$$t_c = \frac{\hat{\beta}_3 - \hat{\beta}_4}{[\hat{\text{Var}}(\hat{\beta}_3) + \hat{\text{Var}}(\hat{\beta}_4) - 2\hat{\text{Cov}}(\hat{\beta}_3, \hat{\beta}_4)]^{1/2}}$$

For a two-tailed test, H_0 is rejected if the numerical value of t_c exceeds t^*_{n-k}(level/2).

e. The major of a student is an important determinant of the GPA because some disciplines are easier to get good grades in and others are more difficult. Also, if a student went to a private school, he or she might have a better training and hence might do better in college. Thus, whether the student went to public or other types of school is important. If a student has to work for a living, then the grades are likely to suffer. Therefore the number of hours of employment might significantly affect the GPA. If a student spends a great deal of time commuting, then the grades might be lower as compared to another person who lives on campus. Not including these variables causes the "omitted variable bias" with biased and inconsistent estimates and forecasts. Furthermore, tests of hypotheses are invalid.

EX 4.9

a. When HLTH increases, people cannot work and are hence likely to retire early. This suggests that $\beta_2 > 0$. If social security income is higher, then the loss in income due to retirement is reduced. We would then expect RETRD to increase and hence $\beta_3 > 0$. If welfare payments go up, people might retire early, suggesting $\beta_4 > 0$. Increase in UNEM means the danger of losing one's job. This might induce some to retire early ($\beta_5 > 0$). People with children under 18 would need income to support them. As retirement reduces income, people might work longer ($\beta_6 < 0$). RACE could have either effect. If nonwhite income is lower than white income, nonwhites might want to work longer and hence retire later. This suggests that β_7 might be negative.

b. The signs for $\beta_3, \beta_6,$ and β_7 are counterintuitive.

c. The test statistics are given by the coefficients divided by the corresponding standard errors and have the t-distribution with 44-7 = 37 d.f. For a 10 percent level, the critical t^* is between 1.684 and 1.697. In the table in the next page if any t-statistic is numerically greater than 1.697, then we would reject the corresponding null hypothesis that the coefficient is zero.

Coefficient		*Std. error*	*Test stat.*	*Reject/Do not rej.*
$\hat{\beta}_1$	- 3.930	9.202	0.427	Do not reject
$\hat{\beta}_2$	1.62738	0.30022	5.421	Reject
$\hat{\beta}_3$	- 0.0005483	0.002081	-0.263	Do not reject
$\hat{\beta}_4$	0.0004568	0.001654	0.276	Do not reject
$\hat{\beta}_5$	0.54853	0.24986	2.195	Reject
$\hat{\beta}_6$	0.15264	0.09686	1.576	Do not reject
$\hat{\beta}_7$	0.07670	0.03390	2.263	Reject

MSSEC, MPUBAS, and DEP are candidates for omission because their coefficients are statistically insignificant.

d. The null hypothesis to test next is that the regression coefficients for MSSEC and MPUBAS are both zero. The test statistic given by Equation (4.3) is

$$F_c = \frac{(ESS_B - ESS_A)/2}{ESS_A/37} = \frac{(175.524 - 175.088)/2}{175.088/37} = 0.046$$

Under the null hypothesis, this has an F-distribution with d.f. 2 for the numerator and 37 for the denominator. From Table A.4a, $F^*(2, 37)$ is between 5.18 and 5.38 and is considerably larger than F_c. Therefore, we cannot reject the null hypothesis but conclude instead that MSSEC and MPUBAS do not have significant effects on RETRD (given the presence of the remaining independent variables). This is consistent with the conclusion in (c) and there is no conflict.

EX 4.11

a. Model C is the restricted model. Also, $n = 40$ and $k = 5$. The test statistic is

$$F_c = \frac{(ESS_C - ESS_A)/2}{ESS_A/(n-k)} = \frac{(44.65914 - 23.510464)/2}{23.510464/35} = 15.742$$

b. Under the null hypothesis, F_c has the F-distribution with 2 d.f. for the numerator and 35 d.f. for the denominator.

c. Reject $H_0: \beta_3 = \beta_5 = 0$ if $F_c > F^*$, the point on $F(2, 35)$ to the right of which is an area equal to 0.1, the level of significance. From the F-table, F^* is between 5.18 and 5.39. Because F_c both values, we reject H_0 and conclude that at least one of the βs is not zero.

d. The test statistic is t with d.f. $n - k = 35$.

e. Because the test says "significantly different from zero," the test is two-tailed. The critical t^* is between 1.684 and 1.697.

f. For PRICE, t_c = -0.071391/0.034730 = -2.0556, which is > t^* in absolute value. Therefore we reject H_0: β_2 = 0 and conclude that it is significantly different from zero.

For INCOME, t_c = 0.003159/0.001763 = 1.7918, which is > t^*. Therefore we reject $H_0: \beta_3 = 0$ and conclude that it is significantly different from zero.

For INTRATE, t_c = -0.153699/0.04919 = -3.1246, which is > t^* in absolute value. Therefore we reject H_0: β_4 = 0 and conclude that it is significantly different from zero.

For UNEMP, t_c = -0.072547/0.298195 = 0.243287 which is < t^*. Therefore we reject H_0: β_5 = 0 and conclude that it is not significantly different from zero.

g. Since β_5 is not significant, UNEMP is a candidate to be dropped from the model. The advantages are, it will (1) increase the d.f. and improve the precision of estimates, and (2) increase the power of tests. The disadvantage is that we might be introducing the *omitted variable bias*. However, since the t-statistic is quite small, the bias is likely to be negligible.

h. Let INCOME* = income in thousands. INCOME* = INCOME/1000 and INCOME = 1000 $\times$ INCOME*. Therefore the coefficient for INCOME* = 1000 $\times$ 0.003159 = 3.159. The corresponding standard error = 1000 $\times$ 0.001763 = 1.763.

i. As price increases, demand will go down. So we expect a negative sign which agrees with the actual sign. If income rises, demand will go up. The expected positive sign is the actual sign also. If the interest rate goes up, it costs more to borrow a card. Hence demand will go down.

The expected sign is negative which is correct. If the unemployment rate increases, people are being laid off which increases uncertainty. Car demand is likely to go down and this the observed effect also.

j. We use model selection criteria to choose among the models. The best model is the one for which the criterion statistic has the lowest value. By this criterion Model B is the best. It is easily verified that this model has all significant coefficients also and the signs are as expected. Thus all criteria suggest Model B as the best.

EX 4.12

	Model A		Model B		Model C	
	Coeff. (std.err)	Test Stat.	Coeff. (std.err)	Test Stat.	Coeff. (std.err)	Test Stat.
Constant	3.913 (0.574)	ignore	4.269 (0.376)	ignore	3.602 (0.533)	ignore
EXPORTS	0.108 (0.082)	1.32 (insig.)				
HOUSTART	0.524 (0.355)	1.48 (insig.)			0.618 (0.360)	1.72 (sign.)
INDPROD	0.525 (0.127)	4.13 (sign.)	0.694 (0.080)	8.68 (sign.)	0.612 (0.091)	6.73 (sign.)
TIMBPRIC	- 0.018 (0.011)	-1.64 (insig.)				
PRODPRIC	- 0.456 (0.087)	-5.24 (sign.)	- 0.556 (0.079)	-7.04 (sign.)	- 0.481 (0.089)	-5.40 (sign.)
d.f.		25		28		27
Critical value		1.708		1.701_		1.703

e. If we use only the model selection statistics, Model A is the best because 4 out of 8 criteria are the lowest for Model A. However, Model A has three insignificant coefficients and is therefore not desirable. If we exclude Model A and compare B and C in terms of selection criteria, Model C is the best for 7 out of 8 criteria. Also, this model has all coefficients significant. Therefore Model C is the best overall. Note that it wrong to use $\bar{R}^2$ as a criterion because it is indirectly the same as using SGMASQ (see Practice Problem 4.3).

f. The three variables with insignificant coefficients are candidates for omission. Thus, EXPORTS, HOUSTART, and TIMBPRIC may be omitted. Omitting these would increase d.f., improve the precision of the other coefficients, and improve the power of tests. The disadvantage is possible *omitted variable bias*. For instance, if we omit only EXPORTS, which was least significant, then the coefficient for HOUSTART becomes significant (see Model C). If we had omitted all three candidates we would have missed this fact. This is why I always recommend eliminating variables one at a time.

g. $H_0: \beta_2 = \beta_3 = \beta_5 = 0.$

h.

$$F_c = \frac{(ESS_B - ESS_A)/3}{ESS_A/(31-6)} = \frac{(7.90322 - 6.22273)/3}{6.22273/25} = 2.25$$

i. Under the null, F_c is distributed as $F(3,25)$.

j. Reject H_0 if $F_c > F^*_{3,25}(0.10) = 2.32$. But $F_c < F^*$. Therefore we do not reject the null. In other words, the coefficients are jointly insignificant.

k. Let EXPORTS* be exports in billions. Since EXPORT is in 100 million board feet, we have EXPORTS* = EXPORTS/10 which gives EXPORTS = 10 EXPORTS*. The only coefficient affected is for EXPORT. The new coefficient for EXPORTS* is 1.08. Its standard error is 0.82. None of the other measures, that is, other coefficients, standard errors, t, F, and R^2 will be affected.

l. Model C explains 74.3 percent of the variation in harvest which means that there might be some missing variables. Other things being equal, an increase of one million in housing starts is expected to increase, on average, timber harvest by 0.618 billion board feet. A one unit increase in industrial production index is expected to increase timber harvest by an average of

0.612 board feet. If the producer price index goes up by one unit, then timber harvest is expected to fall by 0.481 billion board feet. It is surprising that the effect of the price of timber was not statistically significant. Perhaps the presence of the producer price index made this effect negligible.

EX 4.13

a. The null hypothesis for overall significance is that the regression coefficients for HOME, INST, SVC, TV, AGE, AIR, and Y are all zero, that is, $\beta_i = 0$ for i = 2-8. The alternative is that at least one of them is not zero.

b. The test statistic is given by Equation (4.4) and has the value

$$F_c = \frac{(43{,}865.001 - 4923.914)/7}{49.23.914/(40-8)} = 36.15$$

c. Under the null hypothesis, F_c has the F-distribution with d.f. 7 and 32.

d. The critical $F^*(0.01)$ is between 3.12 and 3.30 which is less than F_c. The null hypothesis is therefore rejected.

e-g. For individual coefficients, we carry out a t-test. The critical $t^*_{32}(0.05)$ is between 1.684 and 1.697. If the computed t_c is above this (numerically) we reject the null hypothesis that the corresponding regression coefficient is zero and conclude that the variable has a significant effect on the number of subscribers to cable TV. The following table gives the computed t_c and the criterion.

	Variable	Std. error	Test statistic	Signif./Insign.
HOME	0.406	0.035	11.600	Signif.
INST	- 0.526	0.476	- 1.105	Insign.
SVC	2.039	2.127	0.959	Insign.
TV	0.757	0.688	1.100	Insign.
AGE	1.194	0.503	2.374	Signif.
AIR	- 5.111	1.518	- 3.367	Signif.
Y	0.0017	0.00347	0.490	Insign.

h. The variables INST, SVC, TV, and Y are candidates to be excluded because the corresponding coefficients are not statistically significant.

i. $H_0{:}\beta_i = 0$ for $i = 3\text{-}8$. H_1: At least one of them is not zero.

j.

$$F_c = \frac{(5595.615 - 4923.914)/4}{49.23.914/(40 - 8)} = 1.09$$

k. Under H_0, F_c has F-distribution with d.f. 4 and 32.

l. For a 10 percent test, F^* is between 2.09 and 2.14. Because $F_c < F^*$, we cannot reject the hypothesis. Thus the omitted variables have coefficients that are jointly insignificant.

EX 4.14

a. When the wbase, length, width, height, weight, cyl, liters, and gasmpg increase, the cost of producing a car will go up and hence we would expect the price to go up also. Therefore, we would expect a positive sign for all the regression coefficients. However, for length, width, and height, and liters, the coefficients have unexpected signs. Even in Models B, C, and D, the signs prevail. [Students are not asked for a rationalization, but one possibility is multicollinearity which we will study in Chapter 5.]

b. H_0: $\beta_2 = \beta_4 = \beta_7 = 0 = \beta_8 = \beta_9 = 0$. H_1: At least one of them $\neq 0$

(U) price $= \beta_1 + \beta_2$wbase $+ \beta_3$length $+ \beta_4$width $+ \beta_5$height $+ \beta_6$weight $+ \beta_7$cyl $+ \beta_8$litres $+ \beta_9$gasmpg $+ u$

(R) price $= \beta_1 + \beta_3$length $+ \beta_5$height $+ \beta_6$weight $+ v$

Unrestricted model is A and restricted model is D. Compute

$$F_c = \frac{(ESS_D - ESS_A)/5}{ESS_A/(n-k)} = \frac{(2414.724 - 2303.751)/5}{2303.751/(82-9)} = 0.703$$

From the F-table, $F^*_{5,73}(0.05)$ is between 2.29 and 2.37. Since $F_c < F^*$ we do not reject H_0, that is, we conclude that the effects of the omitted variables are not significantly different from zero.

c. A model is judged by the signs of individual coefficients, their significance and theoretical importance, and the model selection statistics which must be as small as possible. All but HQ and SCHWARZ will choose Model C as the best. If we insist on strict significance at 5% of regression coefficients, Model D will be chosen because in Model C, height and cylinder are significant only at levels slightly above 10%. However, since the *omitted variable bias* cautions us against dropping too many variables and Model C is preferred by the selection criteria, it is chosen as the "best" model.

In Model C, only 57.6 percent of variance in list price is explained. Also, the variables length and height have the wrong signs. There is thus room for improvement in specification. Perhaps there are nonlinear effects. We will also see from the topics in Chapter 5 that, because of high correlation among the explanatory variables, interpreting individual coefficients will be difficult.

d. For overall significance, $H_0: \beta_i = 0$ for $i = 2\text{-}9$. Compute

$$F_c = \frac{R^2/(k-1)}{(1-R^2)/(n-k)} = \frac{R^2/8}{(1-R^2)/73}$$

We need R^2 but have only $\bar{R}^2 = 1 - \frac{n-1}{n-k}(1-R^2)$, from which we solve for R^2 as

$$R^2 = 1 - \frac{n-k}{n-1}(1-\bar{R}^2) = 1 - \frac{73}{81}(1-0.559)$$

$$= 1 - \frac{73}{81}(0.441) = 1 - 0.397 = 0.603$$

Therefore, $F_c = \frac{0.603/8}{(1-0.603)/73} = 13.86$. Under the null hypothesis, F_c has the $F(8,73)$ distribution. $F^*_{8,73}(0.01)$ is between 2.66 and 2.82. Because $F_c > F^*$, we reject H_0 and conclude that at least one of the β's is significantly different from zero.

EX 4.15

a. As the average family size or the percentage of the population with high school or college education increases, we would expect median income to increase also. The more people living in urban areas the higher the expected average income. If unemployment is high in a county, we would expect its median income to be lower. The expected signs are therefore positive for all coefficients except β_5 for which we would expect a negative sign.

b. For overall significance, $H_0\!:\beta_i = 0$ for i = 2-6. Compute

$$F_c = \frac{R^2/(k-1)}{(1-R^2)/(n-k)} = \frac{R^2/5}{(1-R^2)/52}$$

We need R^2 but have only $\bar{R}^2 = 1 - \frac{n-1}{n-k}(1-R^2)$, from which we solve for R^2 as

$$R^2 = 1 - \frac{n-k}{n-1}(1-\bar{R}^2) = 1 - \frac{52}{57}(1-0.837)$$
$$= 1 - \frac{52}{57}(0.163) = 1 - 0.149 = 0.851$$

Therefore, $F_c = \dfrac{0.851/5}{(1-0.851)/52} = 59.4$. Under the null hypothesis, F_c has the $F(5,52)$ distribution. $F^*_{5,52}(0.01)$ is between 3.34 and 3.51. Because $F_c > F^*$, we reject H_0 and conclude that at least one of the β's is significantly different from zero.

c. We note that all the estimated signs agree with our intuition.

d. The null hypothesis is that $\beta_i = 0$ for a typical i from 2 through 6, but separately. The alternative is that it is not zero. The test statistic is t_c which is obtained by dividing the coefficient by the corresponding standard error. Under the null, t_c has the t-distribution with d.f. $n-k$ = 58-6 = 52. For a two-tailed 10% test, the critical $t^*_{52}(0.05)$ is between 1.671 and 1.684. If any computed t_c exceeds this numerically, then we would reject the null hypothesis that the corresponding regression coefficient is zero. For our model, we have

For famsize:	$\lvert t_c \rvert$ = 15.382/3.033 = 5.07
For highschl:	$\lvert t_c \rvert$ = 0.335/0.126 = 2.66
For college:	$\lvert t_c \rvert$ = 0.1.021/0.132 = 7.73
For unemp:	$\lvert t_c \rvert$ = 0.403/0.229 = 1.76
For urb:	$\lvert t_c \rvert$ = 0.029/0.029 = 1.00

The t-statistics for famsize, highschl, college, and unemp, exceed the critical value and hence the corresponding regression coefficient is significantly different from zero. Only the coefficient for urb is insignificant and hence only urb is a candidate for exclusion.

Let medinc* be median income in hundreds of dollars rather than thousands of dollars. Then medinc* = 10 × medinc. This means that all the regression coefficients and the corresponding standard errors will now be multiplied by 10. Also, ESS* = 100 × 640.229 = 64,022.9. Adjusted R^2 is unaffected by the change in units.

f. Since the variables unemp and urb are absent from the second model, the implicit null hypothesis is that $\beta_5 = \beta_6 = 0$ and the alternative that at least one of them is not zero. The test statistic is computed using Equation (4.3) as

$$F_c = \frac{(640.229 - 578.7298)/2}{578.7298/(58-6)} = 2.76$$

Under H_0, this has an F-distribution with d.f. 2 and 52. The critical F^* for a 10% test is between 2.39 and 2.44. Because $F_c > F^*$, we reject the null and conclude that at least one of β_5 and β_6 is different from zero, at the 10% percent level. There is no contradiction between this and the t-test because, according to the latter, unemp had a significant coefficient.

EX 4.17

a. $\bar{R}^2 = 0.277 = 1 - (1-R^2)\frac{n-1}{n-k} = 1 - (1-R^2)\frac{48}{45}$ from which R^2 = 0.322. F_c is now obtained from Equation (4.4). $F_c = 7.1 > F^*_{3,45}(.01)$ and hence the model is significant overall (more specifically, at least one of the coefficients for EDUC, EXPER, and AGE is significant).

b. For a two-tailed test at 1%, t_{45}^{*} is in the range (2.660, 2.704). For a two-tailed test at 10%, t_{45}^{*} is in the range (1.671, 1.684). We see that $t_c > t^*$ for EDUC and EXPER. These are significant at the 1 percent level. But $|t_c| < t^*$ for AGE and hence AGE is not significant even at the 10 percent level.

c. Other things being equal, an older person might be less productive so that the coefficient for AGE may be negative as it is here. However, because this coefficient is insignificant, the negative sign does not mean much.

d. If age is an important determinant of wages, then we would be facing the *omitted variable bias.* This biases estimates and forecasts and also makes them inconsistent. However, since experience indirectly captures the age effect, the insignificance of the age coefficient indicates that we are probably safe in omitting the AGE term without serious consequences.

EX 4.18

The ESL commands for this exercise are given below.

```
ols ENROLL const CATHOL PUPIL WHITE ADMEXP REV
    MEMNEA INCOME COLLEGE ;
omit PUPIL ADMEXP REV MEMNEA INCOME ;
ols ENROLL const CATHOL PUPIL WHITE ADMEXP REV
    MEMNEA INCOME COLLEGE ;
omit REV ;
omit MEMNEA ;
omit PUPIL ;
omit ADMEXP ;
```

One would expect that a state in which the Catholic population is higher than another comparable state is likely to have more students enrolled in private (usually Church) schools (that is, a positive regression coefficient). If the pupil-to-teacher ratio for public schools is higher, we would expect private school enrollment to rise (negative effect). The effect of WHITE is ambiguous a priori and so are those of MEMNEA and COLLEGE. Other things being equal, if administrative expenses are high, one would expect enrollment to suffer (negative effect). If REV goes up, we would expect private school enrollment to go up also (positive effect). The income effect is also likely to be positive.

To save space, I have not attached computer printouts. Instead, just the results are summarized. Students are encouraged to try the above commands and verify the assertions.

The most general model with all the explanatory variables had an adjusted R-square of only 0.458, but the *F*-statistic is highly significant indicating that R-square is not zero. At the 10 percent level of significance, the coefficients for CATHOL, WHITE, and COLLEGE were the only ones significant. Those for PUPIL, ADMEXP, REV, MEMNEA, and, INCOME were insignificant. The Wald *F*-statistic for the joint omission of these variables is 1.19991. Under the null hypothesis, it has an F-distribution with d.f 5 for the numerator and 42 for the denominator. The *p*-value for this is 0.325833. Because it is high, we cannot reject the null hypothesis that all the omitted variables have zero coefficients. As a conservative approach, we start with the original model and omit, one at a time, the following variables: REV, MEMNEA, PUPIL, and ADMEXP. The final model had the best (that is, the lowest) model selection statistics and is chosen for interpretation. It should be noted that the Wald F-test performed above also eliminated INCOME because it had an insignificant coefficient in the original model. However, in the final model the income term is significant at the 6.5 percent level and is retained. This example too points out to the wisdom of not eliminating a whole group of variables but for doing it one at a time. That way, variables which were originally insignificant might become significant because of improved precision due to increased d.f.

The variables with significant coefficients in the final model are: CATHOL, WHITE, INCOME, and COLLEGE. Adjusted R-square was 0.476 indicating that more than 50 percent of the variation in enrollments is unexplained by the model. As expected, CATHOL and INCOME had positive effects. Interestingly, states with greater proportions of whites and college graduates had, on average, decreased private school enrollments.

EX 4.19

The ESL commands for this exercise are given below.

```
ols MORT const INCC POV EDU1 EDU2 ALCC TOBC
   HEXC PHYS URB AGED ;                          [Model A]
```

```
omit INCC EDU1 URB ;                                    [Model B]
ols MORT const INCC POV EDU1 EDU2 ALCC TOBC
  HEXC PHYS URB AGED ;                                  [Model A]
omit EDU1 ;                                             [Model C]
omit INCC ;                                             [Model D]
omit URB ;                                              [Model E]
```

If a state has a higher income than another state then its effect on mortality rates might go either way. For instance, higher incomes means better health care and hence reduced mortality. However, if incomes are high, residents might smoke more and eat more which would contribute to increased mortality. Thus the net effect is ambiguous. Increased poverty, tobacco and alcohol consumption, and elderly population would be expected to increase the mortality rate. Education is likely to improve health and hygiene and hence decrease mortality. If a state has relatively more physicians, one would expected mortality rates to decline. The effect of URB is ambiguous.

The overall adjusted R-square for the most general model is 0.936, very high for cross section data. The coefficients for INCC, EDU1, and URB were insignificant and the Wald F-statistic for omitting them is also insignificant. The restricted model is identical to the one obtained by omitting variables one at a time until all coefficients (ignoring the constant term) are significant at levels below 10 percent. In the final model (E), POV, EDUC2, ALCC, TOBC, HEXC, PHYS, and AGED are significant at levels below 3 percent. However, alcohol consumption, health care expenses, and physicians have counterintuitive signs. The effects of education, tobacco consumption, and elderly population have the expected signs.

EX 4.20

The ESL commands for this problem are given below.

```
ols ATTEND const POP CAPACITY PRIORWIN CURNTWIN
  G1 G2 G3 G4 G5 GF OTHER TEAMS ;                       [Model A]
omit CAPACITY G1 G2 G3 G4 G5 GF ;                       [Model B]
ols ATTEND const POP CAPACITY PRIORWIN CURNTWIN
  G1 G2 G3 G4 G5 GF OTHER TEAMS ;                       [Model A]
omit CAPACITY ;                                         [Model C]
omit G4 ;                                               [Model D]
```

```
omit G2 ;                                   [Model E]
omit GF ;                                   [Model F]
omit G3 ;                                   [Model G]
omit G1 ;                                   [Model H]
```

The population of a city, capacity of the stadium, previous year's win of the home team, and the current year's wins are likely to affect positively the attendance at baseball games. The measure G1 through G5, GF, OTHER, and TEAMS are likely to have negative effects.

The adjusted R-squared of the general model was 0.73, which was extremely significant. The joint F-test for the omission of CAPACITY, G1 through G5, and GF indicates an F-value of 1.711, d.f. 7 and 65, and pvalue of 0.12. Thus, at the 10 percent level, we cannot reject the null hypothesis that all these variables had zero coefficients. As was done before, we omitted variables one at a time and found Model G to be the best in terms of the selection criteria. In this model, POP, PRIORWIN, CURNTWIN, G5, OTHER, and TEAMS had coefficients significant at levels less than 7 percent. All the coefficients had the expected signs. The final model's adjusted R-square was 0.736, which is quite good for a cross section model.

EX 4.21

Use the following ESL commands to obtain the necessary estimates.

```
ols slrygain const tuition z1 z2 z3 z4 z5 ;
omit z4 ;
omit tuition ;
omit z2 ;
omit z3 ;
```

If tuition costs are higher, one would expect that the salary gain would also be higher. Thus we would expect the coefficient for tuition to be positive. All the other regression coefficients are also expected to be positive because a higher rating or evaluation means better training and reputation and hence increased starting salaries after graduation.

From the computer printout for the above, the F-statistic for testing the overall goodness of fit is 2.567414 and the corresponding p-value is 0.056379. This suggests that, at the 6 percent level of significance, we would reject the null hypothesis that all the regression coefficients are zero. At the end of the data-based model reduction procedure in which the variable with the highest p-value is omitted at each step (because it had the least significant coefficient), the "best" final model is as follows.

```
--------------------------------------------------------------------------
VARIABLE        COEFFICIENT          STDERROR     T STAT    2Prob(t > |T|)

constant         62.437508          6.231523   10.019623     < 0.0001 ***
z1               -6.397739          2.103585    -3.04135     0.005991 ***
z5               -5.515992          2.683303   -2.055672     0.051873 *

Error Sum of Sq (ESS) 1494.511511   Std Err of Resid. (sgmahat) 8.242108
Unadjusted R-squared          0.375   Adjusted R-squared              0.318
--------------------------------------------------------------------------
```

This model is chosen as the best because it had the lowest model selection criteria and had all regression coefficients significant at levels below 5.2 percent. However, the results are not credible. Only the MBA skills in being analysts and the curriculum evaluation rating had significant effects but the observed effects were counterintuitive with negative signs. The model is clearly misspecified. Perhaps one should include nonlinear effects. Also, since the model explains only 31.8 percent of the variance of salary gain, omitted variable must be present. [Multicollinearity among the explanatory variables might also be a problem but students haven't studied that topic yet.]

EX 4.22

The ESL commands to answer this question are as follows.

```
ols retrd const hlth mssec mpubas unemp dep race ;
omit mssec ;
omit mpubas ;
ols retrd const hlth mssec mpubas unemp dep race ;
omit mssec mpubas ;
```

The estimates are given in the answers to Exercise 4.9. As shown there, mssec, mpubas, and dep are candidates for omission because their coefficients are statistically insignificant. When mssec and mpubas were omitted, we note that the coefficient for dep becomes significant at the 7.3 percent level. This result teaches us an important lesson, namely, that we should not rush and omit all the variables with insignificant coefficients because we might miss something that might have become significant had we omitted variables one at a time. The Wald F-test part is answered in Exercise 4.9(d). As we see from the answers to Exercise 4.9(a) and (b), the sign for the coefficient of dep is counterintuitive.

EX 4.23

The ESL commands for this problem are given below.

```
ols housing const density value income popchang unemp localtax statetax ;
omit localtax ;
omit unemp ;
omit statetax ;
omit density ;
ols housing const density value income popchang unemp localtax statetax ;
omit localtax unemp statetax density ;
```

For a detailed analysis, see the answers to Exercise 4.10 given in Appendix B.

EX 4.24

To reproduce the table for Exercise 4.12 use the following ESL commands.

```
ols HARVEST const EXPORTS HOUSTART INDPROD
   TIMBPRIC PRODPRIC ;
omit EXPORTS ;
omit TIMBPRIC ;
ols HARVEST const EXPORTS HOUSTART INDPROD
   TIMBPRIC PRODPRIC ;
omit EXPORTS TIMBPRIC ;
```

For a complete analysis of this example see the answers to Exercise 4.12.

EX 4.25

The ESL commands to answer this question are as follows.

```
ols sub const home inst svc tv age air y ;
omit y ;
omit tv ;
omit svc ;
omit inst ;
```

All the other parts are answered in Exercise 4.13.

EX 4.26

The following ESL commands are useful to obtain the empirical results for this exercise.

```
ols medinc const famsize highschl college unemp urb ;
omit urb ;
```

From the answers to Exercise 4.15 we note that in the second model both urb and unemp were omitted. We see from the commands above that if we had omitted just urb then the coefficient for unemp would have become significant at the 10 percent level and would have been the best final model.

EX 4.27

Use the following ESL commands to obtain the computer results.

```
ols chd const cal unemp cig edfat meat spirits beer wine ;
omit wine ;
omit unemp ;
omit meat ;
omit cal ;
ols chd const cal unemp cig edfat meat spirits beer wine ;
omit wine unemp meat cal ;
```

See the answers to Exercise 4.16 in Appendix B for the analysis of this data set.

CHAPTER 5

EXERCISES

EX 5.1

The model is $y_t = \beta_2 x_{t2} + \beta_3 x_{t3} + v_t$, with $x_2 + x_3 = 1$. Substituting $x_3 = 1 - x_2$ in equation (5.3), we have

$$\hat{\beta}_2 \Sigma x_2(1-x_2) + \hat{\beta}_3 \Sigma x_3(1-x_2) = \Sigma y(1-x_2)$$

$$\hat{\beta}_2 \Sigma x_2 - \hat{\beta}_2 \Sigma x_2^2 + \hat{\beta}_3 \Sigma x_3 - \hat{\beta}_3 \Sigma x_2 x_3 = \Sigma y - \Sigma y x_2$$

Because the deviation of a variable from its mean is zero (by Property 2.A.4), Σx_2, Σx_3 and Σy are zero. We readily see that the above equation reduces to equation (5.2), the first normal equation.

EX 5.3

The estimated model is $\widehat{GNP}$ = - 4089.455 + 31.87 *POP*. Substituting this in Model C of Table 5.1,

$$\begin{aligned}\widehat{HOUSING} &= -1315.750 - 184.751\,INTRATE + 14.90\,POP \\ &\quad + 0.52(-4089.455 + 31.87\,POP) \\ &= -3442.27 - 184.751\,INTRATE + 31.47\,POP\end{aligned}$$

We note that the coefficient for *POP* is quite close to that of Model A. The modified constant term is much closer to the constant term than the one in Model C.

EX 5.4

a. The statement is wrong. Although t-tests might indicate individual insignificance, several variables may be jointly significant. If all the insignificant variables are dropped, we are likely to introduce serious omitted variable bias. We saw in Table 5.8 that both LG and LP are insignificant. But when LP was omitted in Model B, LG became significant. If we had eliminated both, we would have committed the specification error of omitting a variable (LG) that belongs in the model.

b. This statement is also wrong. Although multicollinearity (MC) does raise the standard errors, the estimates are unbiased and consistent and the t- and F-distributions are valid. Therefore the tests are valid.

EX 5.5

Yes, we would expect MC between verbal and math SAT scores as well as between HSGPA and the SAT scores, because a student who gets good grades is likely to do well in the SAT. Estimates are still unbiased, consistent, and BLUE, but might have higher standard errors. But the tests are still valid.

EX 5.6

Such a high correlation between W and P indicates severe MC. As in Exercise 5.5, estimates are unbiased, consistent, and BLUE. Because standard errors are likely to be higher, confidence intervals are likely to be wider. Tests are, however, valid.

EX 5.7

To identify MC, compute the correlation coefficients among the explanatory variables. If MC is present, we would notice large values for these correlations. A second way to identify MC is to omit the variable that has the least significant coefficient. If the results for the remaining coefficients changed drastically, MC is surely present. For the data set used in Exercise 4.16, the matrix of correlation coefficients is on the next page (the last column has the variable numbers). Note that quite a few correlations are above 0.9. Thus there is a considerable degree of MC in this data set.

EX 5.8

This statement is erroneous, just the opposite is true. MC increases the standard errors and *lowers* t-statistics. A lower t-statistic is likely to make a variable insignificant rather than significant.

EX 5.9

This statement is not valid because high multicollinearity does not affect the assumptions made on the model and hence the properties of unbiasedness, consistency, and efficiency are unaffected by multicollinearity.

2) cal	3) unemp	4) cig	5) edfat	6) meat	
1.000	-0.400	0.775	-0.883	-0.843	(2
	1.000	-0.526	0.481	0.409	(3
		1.000	-0.914	-0.804	(4
			1.000	0.889	(5
				1.000	(6

7) spirits	8) beer	9) wine	
-0.849	-0.780	-0.805	(2
0.352	0.420	0.512	(3
-0.884	-0.936	-0.943	(4
0.919	0.913	0.948	(5
0.835	0.782	0.798	(6
1.000	0.947	0.934	(7
	1.000	0.974	(8
		1.000	(9

EX 5.10

It was pointed out in Property 4.5 (Section 4.5) that adding an irrelevant variable still yields estimates that are unbiased and consistent. But, because their variance will be higher than that using the true model, the estimates are inefficient. Multicollinearity, in contrast, does not affect any of the properties and hence estimates are also BLUE, that is, efficient. Hence the statement is only partly true.

CHAPTER 6

PRACTICE PROBLEMS

PP 6.1

The slope of a straight line for a linear model is $dY/dX = \beta_2$. Therefore, the elasticity is $\beta_2 X/Y$. From Property 6.2c, the derivative of Y with respect to X in a linear-log model is β_2/X. Therefore the corresponding elasticity is β_2/Y.

PP 6.2

The slope is given by $\Delta Y/\Delta X = \beta_2/X$ which is negative. Also, the absolute value of the slope becomes smaller and smaller as X increases. if $\beta_1 = 0$, the graph will be as drawn below. For positive values of β_1 the curve will shift upward.

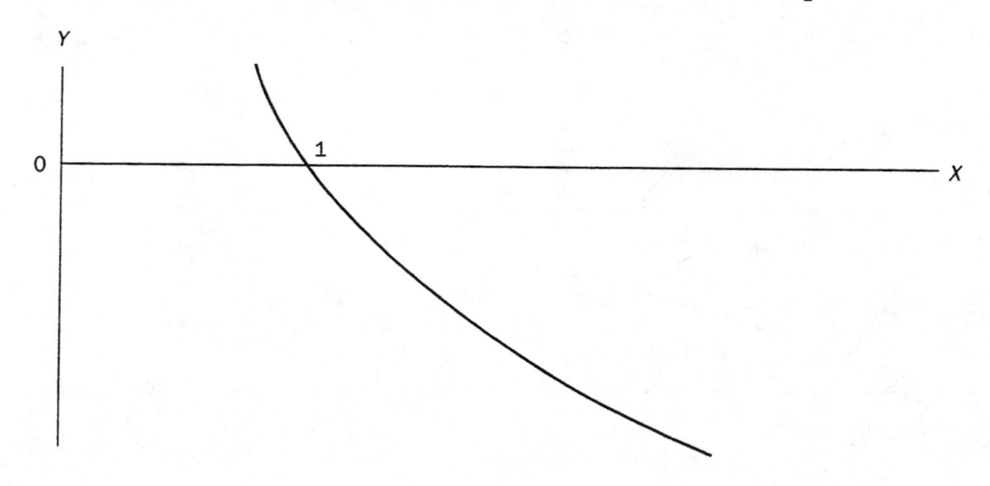

PP 6.3

Let P stand for price and S represent square feet. Then the estimated elasticity is $\eta = (S/\hat{P})\ (d\hat{P}/dS)$.

For the estimated linear model, $d\hat{P}/dS = 0.139$ and $\hat{P} = 52.351 + 0.139\ S$. Substituting these into the expression for elasticity, we get

$$\eta = \frac{0.139\ S}{52.351 + 0.139\ S}$$

For S = 1,500, 2,000, and 2,500, these are respectively 0.799, 0.842, and 0.869.

For the linear-log model,

$$\hat{P} = -1{,}749.974 + 299.972 \ln(S) - 145.094 \ln(BEDRMS)$$

The partial derivative (that is, treating BEDRMS as fixed) of ln(S) with respect to S is 1/S. Therefore $\partial\hat{P}/\partial S$ = 299.972/S. The expression for elasticity now becomes

$$\eta = \frac{299.972}{-1{,}749.974 + 299.972 \ln(S) - 145.094 \ln(BEDRMS)}$$

Assuming that BEDRMS = 4, the elasticities for S = 1,500, 2,000, and 2,500 are respectively, 1.236, 0.9119, and 0.7577. These numbers are quite different from those for the linear model.

PP 6.4

If β_2 is negative, then *Y* increases as *X* increases. Also the absolute value of the slope becomes smaller as *X* increases. The graph will therefore be as follows.

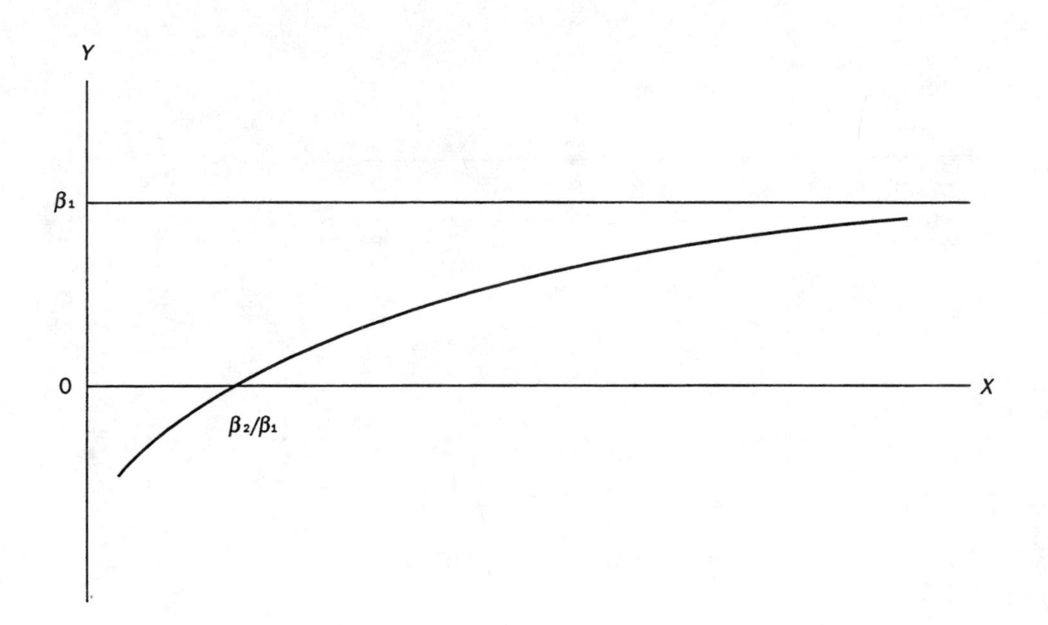

PP 6.6

Practice computer session 6.3 has the commands to answer this question. It is readily seen that the added term BATHS makes the specification inferior to the one without the BATHS term, both in terms of the selection criteria and in terms of the significance of the coefficient for BATHS.

PP 6.7

The slope of this graph is $dY/dX = \beta_2 + 2\beta_3 X$ (see Property 2.A.6). The elasticity follows readily.

PP 6.8

The following commands will be useful for using the ESL program for this exercise.

```
square EDUC EXPER AGE ;
logs WAGE ;
ols l_WAGE const EDUC EXPER AGE sq_EDUC
  sq_EXPER sq_AGE ;
omit EDUC AGE sq_EXPER sq_AGE ;
```

For the omitted variables, the Wald F-statistics is 0.329573. Under the null hypothesis that the omitted variables have zero coefficients, this has an F-distribution with d.f. 4 and 42. The corresponding p-value is 0.856523 which is quite high indicating that we cannot reject the null hypothesis even at the 85 percent level. This means that the omitted variables are probably redundant. If WAGE2 is wages in hundreds of dollars, we have WAGE2 = WAGE/100. Then ln(WAGE2) = ln(WAGE) - ln(100) = ln(WAGE) - 4.605. Substituting this in Equation (6.10), we get

$$\ln(\text{WAGE2}) = 2.418 + 0.005\,\text{EDUC}^2 + 0.024\,\text{EXPER}$$

Thus only the constant term is affected.

PP 6.9

Using Property 6.2c, we have $(1/Y)(dY/dX) = \beta_2 + 2\beta_3 X$. Therefore, the marginal effect is $dY/dX = Y(\beta_2 + 2\beta_3 X) = (\beta_2 + 2\beta_3 X)\exp(\beta_1 + \beta_2 X + \beta_3 X^2)$. The elasticity is $(X/Y)(dY/dX) = X(\beta_2 + 2\beta_3 X)$.

PP 6.10

Holding Z fixed and taking derivatives as before, we get $(1/Y)(\partial Y/\partial X) = \beta_2 + \beta_3 Z$. Therefore, the marginal effect is $\partial Y/\partial X = Y(\beta_2 + \beta_3 Z) = (\beta_2 + \beta_3 Z)\exp(\beta_1 + \beta_2 X + \beta_3 XZ)$. The elasticity is $(X/Y)(\partial Y/\partial X) = X(\beta_2 + \beta_3 Z)$.

PP 6.12

The Cobb-Douglas production function gives rise to the double-log model

$$\ln Q_t = \beta_1 + \alpha \ln K_t + \beta \ln L_t + u_t$$

Substituting $\beta = 1 - \alpha$ in this we get,

$$\ln Q_t = \beta_1 + \alpha \ln K_t + (1-\alpha) \ln L_t + u_t$$

$$= \beta_1 + \ln L_t + \alpha(\ln K_t - \ln L_t) + u_t$$

Bringing $\ln L_t$ (which has no unknown coefficient) to the left-hand side,

$$\ln Q_t - \ln L_t = \beta_1 + \alpha(\ln K_t - \ln L_t) + u_t$$

The procedure is to generate two new variables; $Y_t = \ln Q_t - \ln L_t$ and $X_t = \ln K_t - \ln L_t$. Then regress Y_t against a constant and X_t. $\hat{\beta}$ is obtained as $1-\hat{\alpha}$.

PP 6.13

The ESL commands for this exercise are given below.

```
logs BUSTRAVL FARE GASPRICE INCOME POP DENSITY
   LANDAREA ;
ols l_BUSTRA const l_FARE l_GASPRI l_INCOME l_POP
   l_DENSIT l_LANDAR ;
omit l_DENSIT l_GASPRI l_FARE ;
```

The Wald F-statistic for the omitted variables is = 0.583902, which has the F-distribution with d.f. 3 and 33. The corresponding p-value of 0.629794 indicates that we cannot reject the null hypothesis that the omitted variables have zero coefficients.

PP 6.14

The following ESL commands will be useful here.

```
(* generate the square variables *)
square home inst svc tv age air y ;
(* estimate the most general model using the Hendry/LSE approach *)
ols sub const home inst svc tv age air y sq_home sq_inst sq_svc sq_tv
 sq_age sq_air sq_y ;
(* omit variables one at a time but retaining svc and inst -- either
the linear or the quadratic term *)
omit inst ;
omit tv ;
omit sq_svc ;
```

```
omit age ;
omit sq_home ;
(* after omitting sq_tv, note that svc and sq_inst are the only
variables with insignificant coefficients *)
omit sq_tv ;
(* this is the final model in Example 6.7 and it has lower model
selection statistics than the above model *)
ols sub const home age air y sq_age sq_air sq_y ;
```

The output from the above computer session indicates that at each stage, installation fee and the monthly fee are insignificant. Retaining them till the end results in a model inferior to the final model in Example 6.7. The conclusion is, *given the presence of the other variables*, the installation and monthly fees have insignificant coefficients.

PP 6.15

The modified ESL commands from Practice Computer Session 6.10 are given below.

```
(* First generate the square variables *)
square home inst svc tv age air y ;
(* Final model in Example 6.7 *)
ols sub const home age air y sq_age sq_air sq_y ;
(* generate estimated Y and its powers *)
genr yhat1=sub-uhat
genr yhat2 = yhat1*yhat1
genr yhat3=yhat1*yhat2
genr yhat4=yhat2*yhat2
list
(* estimated model with new variables *)
ols sub const home age air y sq_age sq_air sq_y yhat2 yhat3 yhat4 ;
omit yhat2 yhat3 yhat4 ;
```

The F-test and the t-tests for yhat2, yhat3, and yhat4 show that these are jointly significant and hence there is model misspecification. However, the RESET test does not suggest how to modify the model to eliminate the problem. One alternative might be to add log terms instead of squares to the model.

PP 6.16

The modified ESL commands from Practice Computer Session 6.7 are given below.

```
square EDUC EXPER AGE ;
logs WAGE ;
ols l_WAGE const EXPER sq_EDUC ;
genr yhat = l_WAGE - uhat
genr yhat2=yhat*yhat
genr yhat3=yhat*yhat2
genr yhat4=yhat*yhat3
ols l_WAGE const EXPER sq_EDUC yhat2 yhat3 yhat4 ;
omit yhat2 yhat3 yhat4 ;
```

For the omitted variables, the Wald F-statistics is 0.462062, with a d.f of 3 and 43, and p-value of 0.710234. Such a high value indicates that we do not reject the null hypothesis that yhat2 yhat3 and yhat4 have zero coefficients. In other words, the RESET test suggests no misspecification.

EXERCISES

EX 6.1

a. The marginal effect of Y with respect to X is $\partial Y/\partial X = \beta_2 - \beta_3(1/X^2)$.

b. The elasticity of Y with respect to X is

$$\eta = \frac{X}{Y}\frac{\partial Y}{\partial X} = \frac{X\,[\beta_2 - \beta_3\,(1/X^2)]}{\beta_1 + \beta_2 X + \beta_3(1/X)}$$

c. For graphing we are going to assume, without loss of generality, that $\beta_1 = 0$. All β_1 does is shift the curve up and down. Several cases arise.

<u>$\beta_2 > 0$ and $\beta_3 > 0$</u>

In this case, $\partial Y/\partial X$ is negative for small X and positive for very large X. This suggests that the curve is U-shaped with a minimum when $\partial Y/\partial X = \beta_2 - \beta_3\,(1/X^2) = 0$. This minimum is attained when $X = (\beta_3/\beta_2)^{1/2}$. Y therefore graphs as shown in the next page.

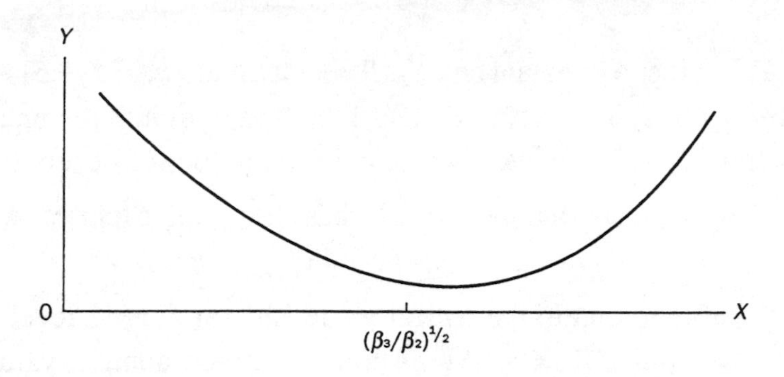

$\beta_2 > 0$ and $\beta_3 < 0$

In this case, $\partial Y/\partial X$ is always positive and the second derivative is always negative. Also, when $X = (-\beta_3/\beta_2)^{1/2}$, $Y = 0$. Therefore the graph is as shown below.

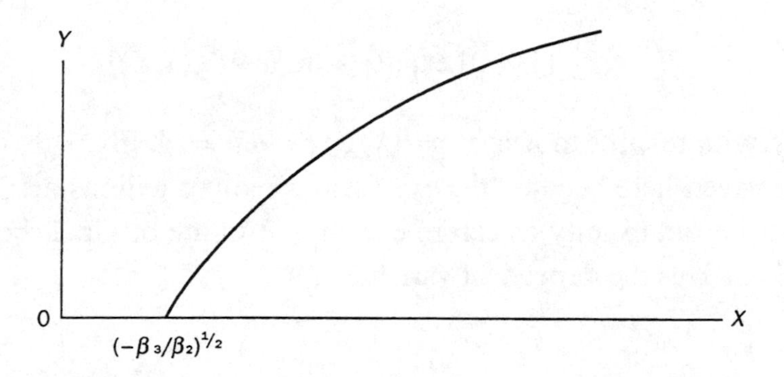

$\beta_2 < 0$ and $\beta_3 > 0$

In this case, $\partial Y/\partial X$ is always negative and when $X = (-\beta_3/\beta_2)^{1/2}$, $Y = 0$. Therefore the curve is as drawn below.

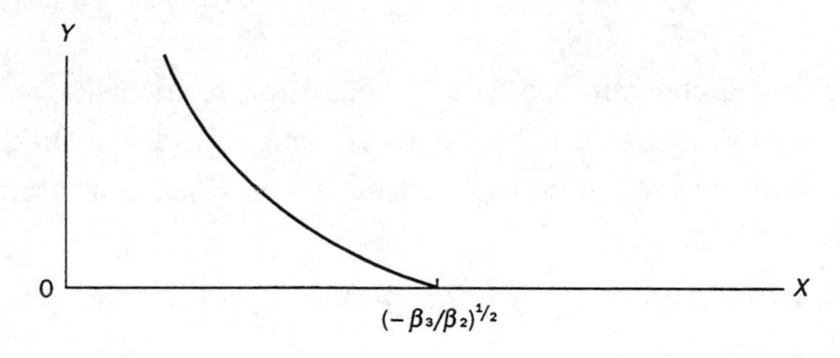

The case when both β_2 and β_3 are negative is ignored because then Y would always be negative (when $\beta_1 = 0$) a situation that does not generally arise in economics.

d. First regress Y_t against a constant and X_t. Then compute $\hat{u}_t = Y_t - \hat{\beta}_1 - \hat{\beta}_2 X_t$. Next regress $\hat{u}_t$ against a constant, X_t, and $1/X_t$, and compute the unadjusted R^2. The test statistic is LM = nR^2, where n is the number of observations.

e. Under the null hypothesis that $\beta_3 = 0$, LM has the χ^2 distribution with one d.f.

f. Look up the χ^2 table to obtain the critical value LM^* at the 5% level and for one d.f. Reject the null if $\text{LM} > \text{LM}^*$. Alternatively, compute p-value = the area to the right of LM^* in χ_1^2. Reject the null if p-value is less than the level of significance.

When $\ln Y$ is the dependent variable, the chain rule of differentiation gives $(1/Y)(\partial Y/\partial X) = \beta_2 - \beta_3(1/X^2)$. Therefore,

$$\frac{\partial Y}{\partial X} = [\beta_2 - \beta_3 (1/X^2)] \exp[\beta_1 + \beta_2 X + \beta_3(1/X)]$$

The elasticity of Y with respect to X is $\eta = (X/Y)\,\partial Y/\partial X = X[\beta_2 - \beta_3(1/X^2)]$. The graph is not derived here because the expressions require tedious derivations. The LM test is carried out exactly as before except that in the original regression $\ln Y$ is used instead of Y as the dependent variable.

EX 6.3

a. We have, $\partial Y/\partial X = \beta_2 + \beta_3(1/X) + \beta_5(Z/X)$. The elasticity follows as

$$\eta = \frac{Y}{X}\frac{\partial Y}{\partial X} = \frac{1}{X}[\beta_2 + \beta_3(1/X)] + \beta_5(Z/X)\,][\beta_1 + \beta_2 X + \beta_3 \ln X + \beta_4 Z + \beta_5(Z \ln X)]$$

b. Regress Y_t against a constant and X_t and obtain the residuals $\hat{u}_t = Y_t - \hat{\beta}_1 - \hat{\beta}_2 X_t$. Next regress $\hat{u}_t$ against a constant, X_t, $\ln X_t$, Z_t, and $Z_t \ln X_t$. Then compute the unadjusted R^2. The test statistic is LM = nR^2, where n is the number of observations.

c. Under the null hypothesis that $\beta_i = 0$ for $i = 3 \ldots 5$, LM has the χ^2 distribution with 3 d.f.

d. Look up the χ^2 table for 3 d.f. to obtain the critical value LM^* at the 5% level. Reject the null if $\text{LM} > \text{LM}^*$. Alternatively, compute p-value = the area to the right of LM^* in χ_3^2 and reject the null if p-value is less than 0.05.

EX 6.4

a. Taking logarithms of both sides of the Cobb-Douglas production function, we get

$$\ln Q_t = \alpha + \beta \ln K_t + \gamma \ln L_t + u_t$$

b. Let $\alpha = \alpha_1 + \alpha_2 t$, $\beta = \beta_1 + \beta_2 t$, and $\gamma = \gamma_1 + \gamma_2 t$. Substituting these in the basic model, we obtain the unrestricted model.

$$\ln Q_t = \alpha_1 + \alpha_2 t + \beta_1 \ln K_t + \beta_2 (t \ln K_t) + \gamma_1 \ln L_t + \gamma_2 \ln (t\, L_t) + v_t$$

c. The variables to be generated are: $\ln Q_t$, $\ln K_t$, $\ln L_t$, $t \ln K_t$, and $t \ln L_t$.

d. The null hypothesis is $\alpha_2 = \beta_2 = \gamma_2 = 0$. The alternative is that at least one of these coefficients is not zero.

e. The test statistic is $F_c = \dfrac{(ESSR - ESSU)/3}{ESSU/(46-6)}$, where ESSR and ESSU are the error sums of squares for the restricted and unrestricted models, respectively.

f. Under the null, F_c has the F-distribution with 3 d.f. for the numerator and 40 d.f. for the denominator.

g. The critical value is $F^*_{3,40}(0.05) = 2.84$.

h. Reject the null hypothesis if $F_c > 2.84$.

EX 6.5

$$\ln E_t = \beta_1 + \beta_2 \ln Y_t + \beta_3 \ln P_t + u_t$$

a. Let $\beta_2 = \alpha_1 + \alpha_2 t$ and $\beta_3 = \alpha_3 + \alpha_4 t$. Substituting this in the model and rearranging terms, we get

$$\ln E_t = \beta_1 + \alpha_1 \ln Y_t + \alpha_2 (t \ln Y_t) + \alpha_3 \ln P_t + \alpha_4 (t \ln P_t) + u_t$$

b. If α_2 or $\alpha_4 \neq 0$, then the corresponding β will not be constant but will be time-varying. Therefore the relevant hypotheses are $H_0: \alpha_2 = \alpha_4 = 0$, H_1: at least one of the coefficients $\neq 0$. First generate several new variables; $E_t^* = \ln E_t$, $Y_t^* = \ln Y_t$, $P_t^* = \ln P_t$, $X_t = t \ln Y_t$, and $Z_t = t \ln P_t$. Next regress E_t^* against a constant, Y_t^*, and P_t^*, and save the error sum of squares as ESSR. Then regress E_t^* against a constant, Y_t^*, X_t, P_t^*, and Z_t and obtain ESSU. Compute the test statistic

$$F_c = \frac{(ESSR - ESSU)/2}{ESSU/(n-5)}$$

Under the null, F_c has the F-distribution with 2 d.f. for the numerator and $n-5$ d.f. for the denominator. From the F-table for the given level of significance look up the critical value F^*. Reject the null hypothesis if $F_c > F^*$.

EX 6.7

a. The basic restricted model is $\ln C = \alpha + \beta \ln Y + u$. Let $\alpha = \alpha_1 + \alpha_2 N$ and $\beta = \beta_1 + \beta_2 N$. Substituting this in the basic model we get the unrestricted model as $\ln C = \alpha_1 + \alpha_2 N + \beta_1 \ln Y + \beta_2 (N \ln Y) + u$.

b. The partial derivative of the new model with respect to N gives

$$\frac{1}{C}\frac{\partial C}{\partial N} = \alpha_2 + \beta_2 \ln Y$$

The elasticity is therefore given by $N(\alpha_2 + \beta_2 \ln Y)$.

c. The null hypothesis is that $\alpha_2 = \beta_2 = 0$ and the alternative is that at least one of these is zero.

d. First regress $\ln C$ against a constant and $\ln Y$ and save the residual as $\hat{u} = \ln C - \hat{\alpha} - \hat{\beta} \ln Y$. Next estimate the auxiliary regression by regressing $\ln C$ against a constant, N, $\ln Y$, and $N \ln Y$ and compute the unadjusted R^2. The test statistic is $LM = nR^2$, where n is the number of observations.

e. Under the null, LM has the chi-square distribution with 2 d.f. Compute p-value = area to the right of LM in the chi-square distribution with 2 d.f. Reject the null if p-value is less than 0.10.

EX 6.8

Taking the logarithm of the sales relation, we have the log-linear model $\ln S_t = \ln S_0 + t \ln(1 + g) + u_t$. Hence $\ln S_0 = 3.6889$ and $\ln(1 + \hat{g}) = 0.0583$. Therefore, $\hat{S}_0 = e^{3.6889} = 40.000822$, and $\hat{g} = e^{0.0583} - 1 = 0.060033$. Hence, the annual average growth $\hat{g}$ is approximately 6 percent. Five years into the future, $\hat{S}_{t+5} = S_t(1 + \hat{g})^5 = 1.3384\, S_t$.

EX 6.9

1. The null hypothesis is $\beta_3 = 1$ and the alternative is that it is $\neq 1$. The test statistic is $t_c = (\hat{\beta}_3 - 1)/$ std error for $\hat{\beta}$. We have $\hat{\beta}_3$/std. error = 0.807/std. error = 7.721. Solving for the standard error, we get the value as 0.807/7.721 = 0.1045201. The t-statistic is now given as t_c = (0.807 − 1)/0.1045201 = −1.85. Under the null hypothesis this has the t-distribution with d.f. $n-k = 31-4 = 27$. The critical value for a two-tailed 5% test is $t^* =$ 2.052. Since $|t_c| < t^*$, we cannot reject the null hypothesis. The conclusion, therefore, is that the elasticity is unitary.

2. Let HOUSESTART* be housing starts in thousands. Then HOUSESTART* = 1000 × HOUSESTART, or HOUSESTART = HOUSESTART*/1000. Taking logarithms we get, ln(HOUSESTART) = ln(HOUSESTART*) − ln(1000). Substituting this in the model we obtain ln(HARVEST) = β_1 + β_2 [ln(HOUSESTART*) − ln(1000)] + ... = [β_1 − β_2 ln(1000)] + β_2 ln(HOUSESTART*) + ... The only change is in the constant term which now becomes 0.856 - [0.807 × ln (1000)] = −4.719.

EX 6.10

a. $$F_c = \frac{(ESSB - ESSA)/2}{ESSA/(40-6)} = \frac{(0.311974 - 0.309293)/2}{0.309293/34} = 0.147$$

b. Under the null hypothesis, this has the F-distribution with 2 d.f. for the numerator and 34 d.f. for the denominator.

c. $F^*_{2,34}(0.10)$ = (2.44, 2.49).

d. Since $F_c < F^*$, we cannot reject the null hypothesis.

e. Not rejecting the null implies that the coefficients for ln(UNEMP) and ln(POP) are jointly insignificant.

f. The t-statistic for ln(PRICE) is given by (1.557 − 1)/0.230 = 2.42. For ln(INCOME) it is (4.807 − 1)/0.708 = 5.38. For ln(INTRATE) it is (0.208 − 1)/0.058 = −13.66.

g. Under the null hypothesis, the t-statistics have the t-distribution with d.f. (for Model B) 40–4 = 36.

h. The critical value t^* for 36 d.f. and 5 percent level is (since the alternative is two-sided) in the range 2.021 to 2.042.

i. Since all the t-statistics are numerically above this we reject the null hypothesis and conclude that the elasticities are significantly different from 1. Since the elasticities for price and income are numerically greater than 1, they are elastic. For interest rate it is inelastic.

EX 6.12

The claim is incorrect. The dependent variable for the double-log model is ln (*COLGPA*) and not *COLGPA*. Therefore R^2 values are not comparable.

First formulate a double-log model

$$\ln(COLGPA) = \gamma_1 + \gamma_2 \ln(HSGPA) + \gamma_3 \ln(SAT) + \gamma_4 \ln(MSAT) + v$$

The regression coefficients are now elasticities. The test procedures are similar to those described in Chapter 4 in the section on linear combination of coefficients.

EX 6.13

a. If schooling has no effect on earnings, the coefficient for S would be zero. ($H_0: \beta = 0$ and $H_1: \beta \neq 0$). The test is a two-tailed t-test with 56 d.f., and $t_c = 0.094/0.005 = 18.8$. We would expect such a high t-statistic to be very significant. At the 1 percent level, $t^*_{56}(0.005)$ is only 2.7. Since $t_c > t^*$ we conclude that schooling is significant at the 1 percent level.

b. If neither schooling nor experience have any effect on earnings, the coefficients for all the explanatory variables (except the constant) will be zero. That is the null hypothesis. The alternative is that at least one of them has a non-zero coefficient. The test is an F-test on the overall significance of the model. the test statistic is given by equation (4.4) as

$$F_c = \frac{0.337/3}{0.663/56} = 9.5$$

$F^*_{3,56}(0.01)$ is approximately 4.1, which is well below F_c. Therefore, we reject the null hypothesis and conclude that the model is significant overall.

c. The null hypothesis is that the coefficients for N and N^2 are both zero. The alternative is that at least one of the coefficients is nonzero. Estimate the restricted model by regressing ln E against a constant and S. Then compute the F-statistic [as in equation (4.3)].

$$F_c = \frac{(ESS_R - ESS_U)/2}{ESS_U/56}$$

which has the F-distribution with 2 and 56 d.f. Reject H_0 if $F_c > F^*_{2,56}(a)$, for the level of significance a.

d. Elasticity of E with respect to S is $(\Delta E/\Delta S)(S/E) = 0.094S$. This can be calculated provided the value of S is known. The elasticity is not constant but varies with S. Elasticity with respect to experience is $(\Delta E/\Delta N)(N/E) = N(0.023 - 0.00065N)$. This varies with N.

EX 6.14

a. As a region's income increases, we would expect the demand for labor to increase also. Income elasticity of employment is positive as expected. When the wage rate rises, the demand for labor is likely to decrease. As expected, wage elasticity is negative. If the local government spends more money, we would expect employment to go up. The elasticity for *GOVTEXP* is also positive as expected.

b. $t^*_{18}(0.005) = 2.878$, $t^*_{18}(0.025) = 2.101$ and $t^*_{18}(0.05) = 1.734$. For significance we need $|t_c| > t^*$. At the 1 percent level, ln(*GOVTEXP*) is the only significant variable. At the 5 percent level, ln(*INCM*) is also significant, and at the 10 percent level ln(*WAGE*) is also significant. The constant term is insignificant even at the 10 percent level.

c. When $\alpha_1 = \alpha_2$ we have,

$$\begin{aligned}\ln EMP &= \alpha_0 + \alpha_1 \ln POP + \alpha_1 \ln (INCM/POP) + \\ &\quad \alpha_3 \ln WAGE + \alpha_4 \ln GOVTEXP + error \\ &= \alpha_0 + \alpha_1 (\ln POP + \ln INCM - \ln POP) + \\ &\quad \alpha_3 \ln WAGE + \alpha_4 \ln GOVTEXP + error \\ &= \alpha_0 + \alpha_1 \ln INCM + \alpha_3 \ln WAGE + \\ &\quad \alpha_4 \ln GOVTEXP + error\end{aligned}$$

which is the original model.

$$\hat{\alpha}_1 = \hat{\alpha}_2 = 0.51,\ \hat{\alpha}_3 = -0.25,\ \text{and}\ \hat{\alpha}_4 = 0.62.$$

d. The wage rate is an important determinant of both the demand for and supply of labor. Hence excluding this variable will cause the "omitted variable bias." Hence, estimates and forecasts will be biased and inconsistent.

EX 6.15

If we use both X_1 and X_2 in the model we will fall into the dummy variable trap with exact multicollinearity because $X_2 = \ln(X^2) = 2\ln X = 2X_1$. The model is therefore not estimable.

EX 6.16

a. In terms of all the model selection criteria except SGMSQ ($\hat{\sigma}^2$), Model C is the best. Also, Model C has significant regression coefficients (ignoring the constant).

b. The null hypothesis is that the coefficients for LP, LG, LU, and LR are all insignificant. The alternative is that at least one of them is significant. We thus test the model for overall significance. The test statistic is given by equation (4.4) as

$$F_c = \frac{0.479/4}{0.521/18} = 4.14$$

which is also reported in Table 4.14. Under the null hypothesis this has an F-distribution with d.f. 4 and 18. $F^*_{4,18}(0.05) = 2.93 < F_c$. Therefore we reject the null hypothesis and conclude that the model is significant overall.

c. To test each regression coefficient, we use the t-test with 18 d.f. $t^*_{18}(0.025) = 2.101$. Only the coefficient for LR is higher in absolute value than this. The conclusion is that the coefficients for LG, LP, and LU are not significant. Although these appear unimportant, we should not rush to drop them all from the model simultaneously. If we do, we might run into the "omitted variable bias" problem discussed in Section 4.5. It is wise to first drop LP, which has the lowest t-value, and then reestimate the model. We note from Model B that LG now becomes significant. The reason for this drastic change in results is given in the next chapter. In Model B, LU is very insignificant and is a candidate to be eliminated. We saw earlier that the resulting model (Model C) is the best.

d. If the variables LP and LU are omitted from Model A, we get Model C. The test is the Wald test given in equation (4.3). We have

$$F_c = \frac{(ESS_C - ESS_A)/2}{ESS_A/18} = 0.64$$

which is less than $F^*_{2,18}(0.10) = 2.62$. Hence LP and LU are candidates for elimination. Again, we should be cautious and eliminate only LP first.

EX 6.17

a. First regress PRICE against a constant, SQFT, and YARD and obtain $\hat{\beta}_1, \hat{\beta}_2$, and $\hat{\beta}_3$. Then compute $\hat{u}$ as PRICE $-\hat{\beta}_1 - \hat{\beta}_2$SQFT $-\hat{\beta}_3$YARD.

b. The test statistic is $LM = nR^2 = 59 \times 0.115 = 6.785$. It is distributed as chi-square with 2 d.f.

c. From the chi-square table we have $LM^* = 5.99146$. Since $LM > LM^*$, we reject the null hypothesis and conclude that either ln(SQFT), or ln(YARD), or both belong in the model.

d. The rule of thumb for inclusion is any new variable with p-value less than 0.50. By this rule, ln(SQFT) should be included. The new model is PRICE $= \beta_1 + \beta_2$SQFT $+ \beta_3$YARD $+ \beta_4$ln(SQFT) + v.

EX 6.18

The following ESL commands would be useful in obtaining the relevant statistics.

```
genr time
(* create the square of time *)          genr tsq = time*time
(* create the cube of time *)            genr t3 = tsq*time
(* create inverse of time *)             genr invt = 1/time
(* generate log of time *)               genr ltime = log(time)
(* generate log of farmpop *)            genr lfarmpop = ln(farmpop)
(* generate logit variable *)
genr logit = ln(farmpop/(100-farmpop))
(* linear Model A *)                     ols farmpop 0 time ;
(* compute mean absolute percentage error *)
genr mapea= mean(100*abs(uhat)/farmpop)
(* quadratic Model B *)                  ols farmpop 0 time tsq;
(* compute mean absolute percentage error *)
genr mapeb= mean(100*abs(uhat)/farmpop)
(* cubic Model C *)                      ols farmpop 0 time tsq t3;
(* compute mean absolute percentage error *)
genr mapec= mean(100*abs(uhat)/farmpop)
(* linear-log Model D *)                 ols farmpop 0 ltime;
(* compute mean absolute percentage error *)
genr maped= mean(100*abs(uhat)/farmpop)
(* reciprocal Model E *)                 ols farmpop 0 invt;
```

```
(* compute mean absolute percentage error *)
genr mapee= mean(100*abs(uhat)/farmpop)
(* log-linear Model F *)                ols lfarmpop 0 time;
(* retrieve sigma squared from model F for bias correction *)
genr sgmasq = $ess/$df
genr yhatf = exp(lfarmpop - uhat + (sgmasq/2))
(* compute prediction error and mean absolute percentage error *)
genr uhatf = farmpop - yhatf
genr mapef= mean(100*abs(uhatf)/farmpop)
(* Log-reciprocal Model G *)            ols lfarmpop 0 invt ;
genr sgmasq = $ess/$df
genr yhatg = exp(lfarmpop - uhat + (sgmasq/2))
(* compute prediction error and mean absolute percentage error *)
genr uhatg = farmpop - yhatg
genr mapeg= mean(100*abs(uhatg)/farmpop)
(* double-log Model H *)                ols lfarmpop 0 ltime ;
(* retrieve sigma squared for model G *)
genr sgmasq = $ess/$df
(* predict levels from model H *)
genr yhath = exp(lfarmpop - uhat + (sgmasq/2))
(* compute prediction error and mean absolute percentage error *)
genr uhath = farmpop - yhath
genr mapeh= mean(100*abs(uhath)/farmpop)
(* Logistic Model I *)                  ols logit 0 time ;
(* retrieve sigma squared for model I *)
genr sgmasq = $ess/$df
(* predict levels from model I *)
genr temp = exp(logit - uhat + (sgmasq/2))
genr yhati=100*temp/(temp+1)
(* compute prediction error and mean absolute percentage error *)
genr uhati = farmpop - yhati
genr mapei= mean(100*abs(uhati)/farmpop)
(* log quadratic model J *)             ols lfarmpop 0 time tsq ;
(* retrieve sigma squared for model J *)
genr sgmasq = $ess/$df
(* predict levels from model J *)
genr yhatj = exp(lfarmpop - uhat + (sgmasq/2))
```

```
(* compute prediction error and mean absolute percentage error *)
genr uhatj = farmpop - yhatj
genr mapej= mean(100*abs(uhatj)/farmpop)
smpl 1948 1948
print -o mapea mapeb mapec maped mapee mapef mapeg mapeh
   mapei mapej ;
```

The mean absolute percentage errors for the various models are given below.

Model A	27.36358	Model E	56.654564	Model H	25.24462
Model B	5.149206	Model F	5.2777700	Model I	5.915649
Model C	3.503441	Model G	61.413645	Model J	4.258677
Model D	9.629098				

The cubic model C is clearly the best in terms of the mean absolute percentage error with an average error of only 3.5 percent.

EX 6.19

The ESL commands for this problem are given below.

```
logs HARVEST EXPORTS HOUSTART INDPROD TIMBPRIC PRODPRIC ;
ols l_HARVES const l_EXPORT l_HOUSTA l_INDPRO l_TIMBPR
   l_PRODPR ;
omit l_EXPORT l_TIMBPR ;
ols l_HARVES const l_EXPORT l_HOUSTA l_INDPRO l_TIMBPR
   l_PRODPR ;
omit l_TIMBPR ;
omit l_EXPORT ;
```

The adjusted R-squared for the general model with all explanatory variables is 0.779 and the F-statistic for overall goodness of fit, with d.f. 5 and 25, is 22.204062. The corresponding p-value is less than 0.0001 indicating high joint significance of the variables in the model.

The Wald F-test was for omitting the variable ln(EXPORT) and ln(TIMBPRIC) which had insignificant coefficients. For the omitted variables, the Wald F-statistic, with d.f. 2 and 25, is 0.65238. It has the p-value of 0.529445 which indicates that the null hypothesis that the coefficients are zero cannot be rejected. If we omit variables one at a time, we end up with the same final model.

The elasticities and the standard errors for the final model are given below.

```
--------------------------------------------------------------------------
VARIABLE          COEFFICIENT        STDERROR        T STAT      PROB t > |T|
constant            0.856311         0.118471       7.228014     < 0.0001 ***
l_HOUSTA            0.156796         0.075632       2.073139     0.047828 **
l_INDPRO            0.807003         0.104521       7.720963     < 0.0001 ***
l_PRODPR           -0.41498          0.067974      -6.104949     < 0.0001 ***
Error Sum of Sq (ESS) 0.129252     Std Err of Resid. (sgmahat) 0.069189
Unadjusted R-squared  0.807        Adjusted R-squared              0.785
F-statistic (3, 27)          37.53845      Prob. F > 37.538 is < 0.0001
--------------------------------------------------------------------------
```

To perform the test for unitary elasticity, the t-statistics are given below.

ln(HOUSTART) (1 - 0.156796)/0.075632 = 11.15 Reject H_0
ln(INDPROD) (1 - 0.807003)/0.104521 = 1.85 Do not reject H_0
ln(PRODPRIC) (1 - 0.414980)/0.067974 = 8.6 Reject H_0

Let HOUSETART2 be housing starts in thousands. Then HOUSTART2 = 1000 HOUSTART and ln(HOUSTART2) = ln(1000) + ln(HOUSTART). Therefore, the only coefficient that will change is the constant term which will now become ln(1000) + 0.856311 = 7.764.

EX 6.20

The ESL commands for this problem are given below.

```
logs housing density value income localtax statetax popchang unemp ;
ols l_housin const l_densit l_value l_income l_localt l_statet l_unemp ;
omit l_value ;
omit l_unemp ;
omit l_statet ;
omit l_localt ;
```

The adjusted R-squared for the general model with all explanatory variables is only 0.325 and the F-statistic for overall goodness of fit, with d.f. 6 and 33, is 4.126922. The corresponding p-value is 0.00337 indicating joint significance of the variables in the model at levels below 1 percent.

If we omit variables one at a time and use the model selection criteria to choose the final model, only the variables ln(density) and ln(income) are left. The elasticities and the standard errors for the final model are given below.

```
----------------------------------------------------------------------
VARIABLE          COEFFICIENT        STDERROR       T STAT      2Prob(t > |T|)
constant           3.114683          3.338572      0.932939       0.3569
l_densit          -0.68306           0.210671     -3.242313       0.002513 ***
l_income           2.877763          0.833845      3.451198       0.001412 ***
Error Sum of Sq (ESS) 40.231347   Std Err of Resid. (sgmahat) 1.042753
Unadjusted R-squared    0.395     Adjusted R-squared           0.363
----------------------------------------------------------------------
```

To perform the test for unitary elasticity (ignoring the sign of a coefficient), the t-statistics are given below.

ln(income) $\quad$ (2.877763 - 1)/0.833845 = 2.25

ln(density) $\quad$ (1 - 0.68306)/0.213669 = 1.48

Under the null hypothesis of unitary elasticity, these are distributed as the t-distribution with 40 – 3 = 37 d.f. The critical t^* for a 5 percent test is between 2.021 and 2.042. We readily see that the hypothesis is rejected for income but not for density. Thus, income elasticity is significantly different from 1 but density elasticity is not.

EX 6.21

The ESL commands for this problem are given below.

```
logs ENROLL ;
ols l_ENROLL const CATHOL PUPIL WHITE ADMEXP REV
   MEMNEA INCOME COLLEGE ;
omit PUPIL ADMEXP REV MEMNEA INCOME ;
ols l_ENROLL const CATHOL PUPIL WHITE ADMEXP REV
   MEMNEA INCOME COLLEGE ;
omit REV ;
omit MEMNEA ;
omit PUPIL ;
omit ADMEXP ;
```

The adjusted R-squared for the general model with all explanatory variables is 0.396 and the F-statistic for overall goodness of fit, with d.f. 8 and 42, is 5.094125. The corresponding p-value is less than 0.001 indicating high joint significance of the variables in the model.

The Wald F-test was for omitting the variables PUPIL, ADMEXP, REV, MEMNEA, and INCOME. For the omitted variables, the Wald F-statistics, with d.f. 5

and 42, is 1.256754. It has the p-value of 0.300444 which indicates that the null hypothesis that the coefficients are zero cannot be rejected. If we omit variables one at a time, we note that we would retain the INCOME variable which was insignificant in the general model. Also, the variables omitted for the log-linear model used here are the same as those for linear model of Exercise 4.18.

EX 6.22

The ESL commands for this problem are given below.

```
logs ATTEND POP CAPACITY PRIORWIN CURNTWIN
   G1 G2 G3 G3 G4 G5 GF OTHER TEAMS ;
ols l_ATTEND const l_POP l_CAPACI l_PRIORW
   l_CURNTW l_TEAMS G1 G2 G3 G4 G5 GF OTHER ;
omit l_CAPACI G1 G2 G3 G5 GF ;
ols l_ATTEND const l_POP l_CAPACI l_PRIORW
   l_CURNTW l_TEAMS G1 G2 G3 G4 G5 GF OTHER ;
omit l_CAPACI ;
omit G1 ;
omit G5 ;
omit G2 ;
omit G3 ;
omit GF ;
```

The adjusted R-squared for the general model with all explanatory variables is 0.714 and the F-statistic for overall goodness of fit, with d.f. 12 and 65, is 17.057202. The corresponding p-value is less than 0.0001 indicating high joint significance of the variables in the model. If variables are omitted one at a time based on insignificance of coefficients, the final model is given in the next page. It will be noted that, compared to the linear model in Exercise 4.15 which had G5 in its final model, here G4 is in the final model. Other qualitative results are, however, similar.

EX 6.23 and 6.24

No answers are provided because this is an open-ended question.

EX 6.25

The ESL commands given in Exercise 6.18 are easily modified to carry out the analyses with these data sets.

VARIABLE	COEFFICIENT	STDERROR	T STAT	PROB t > |T|	
constant	-3.196022	1.296864	-2.464423	0.016146	**
l_POP	0.43225	0.098944	4.368641	< 0.0001	***
l_PRIORW	0.818385	0.192251	4.256849	< 0.0001	***
l_CURNTW	0.90735	0.270266	3.35725	0.001268	***
l_TEAM	-0.312646	0.093576	-3.341081	0.001333	***
G4	-0.013384	0.004401	-3.041421	0.003298	***
OTHER	-0.201473	0.072871	-2.764802	0.007252	***

Error Sum of Sq (ESS) 2.602806 Std Err of Resid. (sgmahat) 0.191466

Unadjusted R-squared 0.746 Adjusted R-squared 0.724

F-statistic (6, 71) 34.711771 Prob. F > 34.712 is < 0.0001

CHAPTER 7

PRACTICE PROBLEMS

PP 7.2

The output for this is obtained from Practice Computer Session 7.4 (see Appendix D). In terms of the model selection criteria, the model with ln(*SQFT*) and *POOL* is the best in all cases. The estimated "final" model is

$$\widehat{PRICE} = -\ 1794.475 + 278.329 \ln(SQFT) + 58.444\ POOL$$
$$(-9.35) \qquad (10.96) \qquad\qquad (3.78)$$
$$\bar{R}^2 = 0.904 \qquad\qquad d.f. = 11$$

The marginal effect of SQFT on PRICE is given by

$$\frac{\Delta \widehat{PRICE}}{\Delta SQFT} = \frac{278.329}{SQFT}$$

which, as was conjectured, decreases as *SQFT* increases.

PP 7.3

In the model $Y = \beta_1 A_1 + \beta_2 A_2 + \beta_3 A_3 + \beta X + u$, use the relation $A_3 = 1 - A_1 - A_2$. We obtain, $Y = \beta_1 A_1 + \beta_2 A_2 + \beta_3(1{-}A_1{-}A_2) + \beta X + u = \beta_3 + (\beta_1{-}\beta_3)\, A_1 + (\beta_2{-}\beta_3)\, A_2 + \beta X + u$. Therefore, $\hat{\alpha}_0 = \hat{\beta}_3$, $\hat{\alpha}_1 = \hat{\beta}_1 - \hat{\beta}_3$, and $\hat{\alpha}_2 = \hat{\beta}_2 - \hat{\beta}_3$.

PP 7.5

The values for the dummy variables are, $A_1 = 1, H = 1, E_2 = 1, O_3 = 1$, and zero for the others. The estimated relation is $\hat{Y} = \hat{\beta}_0 + \hat{\beta}_1 + \hat{\beta}_3 + \hat{\beta}_5 + \hat{\beta}_8 + \hat{\beta}_{10} X$.

PP 7.7

By proceeding as was done in the Analysis of Variance section we get the following 12 interdependent equations.

$$\begin{aligned}
\mu + a_1 + b_1 &= \alpha_0 + \alpha_1 + \beta_1 \\
\mu + a_1 + b_2 &= \alpha_0 + \alpha_1 + \beta_2 \\
\mu + a_1 + b_3 &= \alpha_0 + \alpha_1 + \beta_3 \\
\mu + a_1 + b_4 &= \alpha_0 + \alpha_1
\end{aligned}$$

$$\begin{aligned}
\mu + a_2 + b_1 &= \alpha_0 + \alpha_2 + \beta_1 \\
\mu + a_2 + b_2 &= \alpha_0 + \alpha_2 + \beta_2 \\
\mu + a_2 + b_3 &= \alpha_0 + \alpha_2 + \beta_3 \\
\mu + a_2 + b_4 &= \alpha_0 + \alpha_2 \\
\mu + a_3 + b_1 &= \alpha_0 + \beta_1 \\
\mu + a_3 + b_2 &= \alpha_0 + \beta_2 \\
\mu + a_3 + b_3 &= \alpha_0 + \beta_3 \\
\mu + a_3 + b_4 &= \alpha_0
\end{aligned}$$

Add all the equations and note that $\Sigma a_j = \Sigma b_k = 0$. We get $\mu = \alpha_0 + \frac{1}{3}(\alpha_1 + \alpha_2) + \frac{1}{4}(\beta_1 + \beta_2 + \beta_3)$. By adding the first four equations we can solve for a_1. By adding the next four equations a_2 can be obtained. a_3 is obtained as $-a_1 - a_2$. Once μ and a_1 are obtained, the first four equations can be used to solve for the b's.

PP 7.8

Let $D_4 = 1$ if the season is the fall and 0 otherwise. If summer is the control quarter, we use D_1, D_2, and D_4. Let $\alpha = a_0 + a_1 D_1 + a_2 D_2 + a_4 D_4$, and $\beta = b_0 + b_1 D_1 + b_2 D_2 + b_4 D_4$. The unrestricted model is now

$$E = a_0 + a_1 D_1 + a_2 D_2 + a_4 D_4 + b_0 T + b_1 D_1 T + b_2 D_2 T + b_4 D_4 T + u$$

Any hypothesis can now be formulated in terms of the a's and b's. For instance, the hypothesis that fall and spring are alike translates to the hypothesis $a_2 = a_4$ and $b_2 = b_4$, which can be tested with a Wald F-test. (Derive the restricted model for this.)

PP 7.10

The intercept will be the same in all the periods if and only if $\alpha_1 = \alpha_2 = 0$. The restricted model is

$$\ln C = \alpha_0 + \beta_0 \ln P + \beta_1 (D_1 \ln P) + \cdots + u$$

The test is the familiar Wald test.

PP 7.11

The unrestricted model is now

$$\ln C = a_0 + a_2 D_2 + a_3 D_3 + b_0 \ln P + b_2 (D_2 \ln P)$$

$$+ b_3(D_3 \ln P) + \cdots + u$$

Since $D_3 = D_1 - D_2$, we have

$$\ln C = a_0 + a_2 D_2 + a_3(D_1 - D_2) + b_0 \ln P$$

$$+ b_2 D_2 \ln P + b_3(D_1 - D_2) \ln P + \cdots + u$$

$$= a_0 + a_3 D_1 + (a_2 - a_3) D_2 + b_0 \ln P$$

$$+ b_3 D_1 \ln P + (b_2 - b_3) D_2 \ln P + \cdots + u$$

It follows that $a_0 = \alpha_0$, $a_3 = \alpha_1$, $a_2 - a_3 = \alpha_2$, $b_0 = \beta_0$, $b_3 = \beta_1$, and $b_2 - b_3 = \beta_2$. The a's and b's are easily estimated from the α's and β's and vice versa.

EXERCISES

EX 7.1

Note that $D2 = 1 - D1$. Substituting this in the second model we get

$$Y = \beta_1 + \beta_2(1 - D1) + \beta_3 X + \beta_4[(1 - D1)X] + u$$

$$= (\beta_1 + \beta_2) - \beta_2 D1 + (\beta_3 + \beta_4) X - \beta_4(D1{*}X)$$

It follows from this that $\alpha_1 = \beta_1 + \beta_2, \alpha_2 = -\beta_2, \alpha_3 = (\beta_3 + \beta_4)$, and $\alpha_t = -\beta_4$.

EX 7.3

a. High correlation among independent variables does not affect the assumptions on the model. Therefore all the properties of the estimates still hold and hypothesis testing is valid.

b.

$$\widehat{LNWAGE} = 0.448 + 0.0795\,SCHOOL + 0.059\,EXP - 0.00076\,EXP^2$$

$$+ 0.18725\,URBAN - 0.04393 + 0.03173$$

Combining constant terms, we get

$$\widehat{LNWAGE} = 0.4358 + 0.0795\,SCHOOL + 0.059\,EXP - 0.00076\,EXP^2$$

$$+ 0.18725\,URBAN$$

c. Differentiating both sides of the estimated model partially with respect to EXP,

$$\frac{1}{\hat{WAGE}} \frac{\partial \hat{WAGE}}{\partial EXP} = 0.059 - 0.00152\, EXP$$

The elasticity is

$$\frac{EXP}{\hat{WAGE}} \frac{\partial \hat{WAGE}}{\partial EXP} = EXP(0.059 - 0.00152\, EXP)$$

$$= 5(0.059 - 0.00152 \times 5) = 0.257$$

EX 7.5

a. Define the dummy variable $H = 1$ if owning a home and 0 otherwise. Let $\alpha = \alpha_0 + \alpha_1 H + \alpha_2 N$; $\beta = \beta_0 + \beta_1 Y + \beta_2 H + \beta_3 N$. Substituting in Model A, we get Model B.

$$C = \alpha_0 + \alpha_1 H + \alpha_2 N + Y(\beta_0 + \beta_1 Y + \beta_2 H + \beta_3 N) + u$$

$$= \alpha_0 + \alpha_1 H + \alpha_2 N + \beta_0 Y + \beta_1 Y^2 + \beta_2 HY + \beta_3 YN + u$$

We need to generate the variables Y^2, HY, and YN.

b. *Renter* ($H = 0$): $\hat{C} = \hat{\alpha}_0 + \hat{\alpha}_2 N + \hat{\beta}_0 Y + \hat{\beta}_1 Y^2 + \hat{\beta}_3 YN$

Home owner ($H = 1$):
$\hat{C} = \hat{\alpha}_0 + \hat{\alpha}_1 + \hat{\alpha}_2 N + \hat{\beta}_0 Y + \hat{\beta}_1 Y^2 + \hat{\beta}_2 Y + \hat{\beta}_3 YN$

$$= (\hat{\alpha}_0 + \hat{\alpha}_1) + \hat{\alpha}_2 N + (\hat{\beta}_0 + \hat{\beta}_2)Y + \hat{\beta}_1 Y^2 + \hat{\beta}_3 YN$$

c. $H_0: \alpha_2 = \beta_3 = 0$. H_1: at least one of them is not zero.

$$C = \alpha_0 + \alpha_1 H + \beta_0 Y + \beta_1 Y^2 + \beta_2 HY + error$$

d.

Step 1: Regress C against a constant, H, N, Y, Y^2, HY, and YN and save the error sum of squares as ESSU.

Step 2: Regress C against a constant, H, Y, Y^2, and HY and save the error sum of squares as ESSR.

Step 3: Compute $F_c = \dfrac{(ESSR - ESSU)/2}{ESSU/(40-7)}$.

e. Under the null hypothesis, $F_c \sim F_{2,33}$.

f. Compute p-value = area to the right of F_c in $F_{2,33}$. Reject H_0 if p-value < 0.05.

g. For income, $\partial C/\partial Y = \beta_0 + 2\beta_1 Y + \beta_2 H + \beta_3 N$. For non-homeowners, we have $H = 0$ and hence $\partial C/\partial Y = \beta_0 + 2\beta_1 Y + \beta_3 N$. For homeowners, we have $H = 1$ and hence $\partial C/\partial Y = (\beta_0 + \beta_2) + 2\beta_1 Y + \beta_3 N$.

For family size, $\partial C/\partial N = \alpha_2 + \beta_3 Y$ for both homeowners and non-homeowners.

h. H_0: $\alpha_1 = \alpha_2 = \beta_1 = \beta_2 = \beta_3 = 0$.

i.

Step 1: Regress C against a constant and Y.

Step 2: Save the error term as $\hat{u} = C - \hat{\alpha} - \hat{\beta} Y$.

Step 3: Regress $\hat{u}$ against a constant, H, N, Y, Y^2, HY, and YN.

Step 4: Compute LM = 40 R^2, where R^2 is the unadjusted R^2 from Step 3.

j. Under the null hypothesis given in (h), LM $\sim \chi_5^2$ and the critical value is $LM^* = 11.0705$.

k. Reject H_0 if $LM > LM^*$.

l. From the regression in Step 3 above select new variables with p-values less than 0.5. Then regress C against a constant, Y, plus the new variables selected above. Then omit variables one at a time based on insignificance of coefficient, until all coefficients are significant. Then use model selection statistics, significance of coefficients, and the omitted variable bias to choose the best model.

m. Let $Y^* = 10Y$. Then $Y = Y^*/10$. Substitute this in Model B.

$$C = \alpha_0 + \alpha_1 H + \alpha_2 N + \beta_0 Y^*/10 + \beta_1 (Y^*)^2/100 + \beta_2 HY^*/10 + \beta_3 Y^* N/10 + u$$

Thus, α_0, α_1, and α_2 are unchanged. β_0, β_2, and β_3 are divided by 10 and β_1 is divided by 100.

EX 7.6

a. Define the dummy variables VHF = 1 for a VHF station, 0 otherwise, ABC = 1 if the station is affiliated with ABC, CBS = 1 for a CBS station, and NBC = 1 for an NBC station, the control being other stations. Define β = b0 + b1 VHF + b2 ABC + b3 CBS + b4 NBC. Substituting in the original model we get the unrestricted model.

$$\text{SHARE} = \alpha + (\text{b0} + \text{b1 VHF} + \text{b2 ABC} + \text{b3 CBS} + \text{b4 NBC})\ \text{NSTAT} + \gamma\ \text{CABLE} + u$$

$$= \alpha + \text{b0 NSTAT} + \text{b1 VHF*NSTAT} + \text{b2 ABC*NSTAT} + \text{b3 CBS*NSTAT} + \text{b4 NBC*NSTAT} + \gamma\ \text{CABLE} + u$$

For this, we should generate new variables Z1 = VHF*NSTAT, Z2 = ABC*NSTAT, Z3 = CBS*NSTAT, and Z4 = NBC*NSTAT.

b. The null hypothesis is that b1, b2, b3, and b4 are all zero. The alternative is that at least one of them is not zero.

c. First regress SHARE against the constant term, NSTAT, and CABLE and save the residuals as UR = SHARE $-\hat{\alpha} - \hat{\beta}\, NSTAT - \hat{\gamma}$ CABLE. Next regress UR against the constant term, NSTAT, CABLE, Z1, Z2, Z3, and Z4. This is the auxiliary regression. Then compute LM = nR^2 which is the number of observations (40 here) multiplied by the unadjusted R-square of the auxiliary regression.

d. LM is distributed as Chi-square with d.f. 4. Look up the Chi-square table for 4 d.f. and find the value to the right of which is an area equal to the level of significance. Reject H_0 if LM is larger than this. Alternatively, compute P(χ_4^2 > LM) and reject the null if this is less than the level of significance.

e. In the auxiliary regression identify the added variables Z's that has coefficients with p-values less than 0.5. Add these to the basic model and estimate it. Then eliminate variables with insignificant coefficients one at a time until the model selection statistics don't improve any more.

EX 7.7

a. The control season is Winter because no dummy variable has been defined for it.

b. When the price of a car goes up, we would expect sales to decline so that $\beta < 0$. Income will have a positive effect and so $\gamma > 0$. If the interest rate goes up, then the cost of financing a car goes up and hence the demand for cars will decrease. Thus, we would expect $\delta < 0$.

c. Let $\alpha =$ a0 + a1 SPRING + a2 SUMMER + a3 FALL. Substituting this in the basic model we get the unrestricted Model (U) as LPCCARS = a0 + a1 SPRING + a2 SUMMER + a3 FALL + β LPRICE + γ LPCINCOME + δ LINTRATE + error. This is the same as Model B.

d. H_0: a1 = a2 = a3 = 0. H_1: at least one of them is not zero.

e. Compute $F_c = \dfrac{(0.31044 - 0.17699)/3}{0.17699/(40-7)} = 8.29$.

f. $F_c \sim F(3,33)$.

g. From the F-table for 1 percent level look up $F^*_{3,33}$ as a value between 4.31 and 4.51.

h. Since $F_c > F^*$, we reject the null hypothesis.

i. To decide on the variables to exclude, we can do a t-test. The degrees of freedom for the t-statistics in Model B in the table is 33. For a 1 percent level of significance, the critical value t^* is in the range (2.704, 2.750). Any variable with a corresponding t-statistics below this (numerically) is a candidate to be dropped. According to this rule, we would drop SUMMER and FALL. This would result in Model C.

j. The model with the lowest model selection statistics is preferable as the best. Six out of the eight criteria choose Model C as the best. Another criterion to use is the significance of the coefficients. All the coefficients in Model C are highly significant. Also, the signs for the coefficients agree with our intuition. Thus, Model C would be chosen as the best model.

k. Let $\beta =$ b0 + b1 SPRING + b2 SUMMER + b3 FALL. Substituting this in Model B we get the unrestricted Model (D) as LPCCARS = a0 + a1 SPRING + a2 SUMMER + a3 FALL + b0 LPRICE + b1 (SPRING * LPRICE) + b2 (SUMMER * LPRICE) + b3 (FALL * LPRICE) + γ LPCINCOME + δ LINTRATE + error.

l. H_0: b1 = b2 = b3 = 0.

m. First regress LPCCARS against all the explanatory variables in Model B and save the error sum of squares as ESSB. Next create Z1 = SPRING * LPRICE, Z2 = SUMMER * LPRICE, and Z3 = FALL * LPRICE. Then regress LPCCARS against the variables in Model B plus the three Z's and save the error sum of squares as ESSD. Next compute

$$F_c = \frac{(ESSB - ESSD)/3}{ESSD/(40-10)}$$

Under the null $F_c \sim F(3, 30)$. From the F-table for 1 percent level look up $F^*_{3,30}$ as 4.51. If $F_c > 4.51$ we would reject the null hypothesis.

n. Ignoring the negative sign of the coefficient, compute $t_c = \dfrac{(\hat{\beta} - 1)}{\text{stderror}}$. Since the standard error is not given directly, we obtain it as stderror = coeff/t-statistics = 1.760/9.6 = 0.183. From this, we have $t_c = = \dfrac{1.760 - 1}{0.183} = 3.99$. Under the null hypothesis this has a t-distribution with d.f. $40 - 5 = 35$. For a 1 percent test, t^*_{35} is in the range (2.704, 2.750). Since t_c exceeds this, we would reject the null. Since the observed elasticity is numerically greater than 1, we conclude that demand is price elastic.

EX 7.8

The model is $P_t = \alpha + \beta S_t + u_t$. We are given quarterly data for 20 years. Therefore, n is 80.

a. Define three dummy variables, D1 = 1 for winter, 0 for other seasons, D2 = 1 for spring, 0 for other seasons, and D3 = 1 for summer, and 0 for other seasons. The control season is fall which has zero values for all three dummy variables. Let α = a0 + a1 D1 + a2 D2 + a3 D3 and β = b0 + b1 D1 + b2 D2 + b3 D3. Substitute this in the model and get

$$\begin{aligned} P_t &= a0 + a1\ D1 + a2\ D2 + a3\ D3 + S_t\ (b0 + b1\ D1 + b2\ D2 + b3\ D3) + u_t \\ &= a0 + a1\ D1 + a2\ D2 + a3\ D3 + b0\ S_t + b1\ (S_t{*}D1) + b2\ (S_t{*}D2) \\ &\quad + b3\ (S_t{*}D3) + u_t \end{aligned}$$

b. H_0: a1 = a2 = a3 = b1 = b2 = b3 = 0. H_1: at least one of these is not zero.

c. For the Wald approach, we would first regress P_t against a constant and S_t and save the residual sum of squares (ESSR) for the restricted model. This regression has $n-2 = 78$ d.f. Next generate the interaction terms D1*S_t, D2*S_t, and D3*S_t. Then regress P_t against a constant, D1, D2, D3, and the above interaction terms. Save the error sum of squares as ESSU. This regression has $n-8 = 72$ d.f. Next compute

$$F_c = \frac{(\text{ESSR} - \text{ESSU})/6}{\text{ESSU}/72}$$

Under the null hypothesis, this has an F-distribution with 6 d.f. for the numerator and 72 d.f. for the denominator. Look up the F-table for the selected level of significance and d.f. 6 and 72 and find F^* the critical value. Reject H_0 if $F_c > F^*$. Equivalently, compute p-value = $P(F > F_c)$ and reject H_0 if p-value is less than the level of significance.

d. For the LM test approach, we would first regress P_t against a constant and S_t and save the residuals as $\hat{u}_t = P_t - \hat{\alpha} - \hat{\beta} S_t$. Then regress $\hat{u}_t$ against a constant, D1, D2, D3, and the interaction terms D1*S_t, D2*S_t, and D3*S_t (this is the auxiliary regression). Next compute LM = the number of observations (80 here) multiplied by the unadjusted R-squared in the auxiliary regression. Under H_0 this has a Chi-squared distribution with 6 d.f. Look up χ^2_6 and find the critical value for the chosen level of significance. Reject H_0 if LM is larger than this critical value. Alternatively, compute $P(\chi^2_6 > \text{LM})$ and reject H_0 if the probability is less than the level of significance.

EX 7.9

a. Define $D = 1$ for a socialist country, 0 otherwise. Let $a = a_0 + a_1 D$, $b = b_0 + b_1 D$, $c = c_0 + c_1 D$, $d = d_0 + d_1 D$, $e = e_0 + e_1 D$, $f = f_0 + f_1 D$, and $g = g_0 + g_1 D$. We then have,

$$\begin{aligned} Y &= a_0 + a_1 D + (b_0 + b_1 D)\, GDP + (c_0 + c_1 D)\, POP + (d_0 + d_1 D)\, URB \\ &\quad + (e_0 + e_1 D)\, LIT + (f_0 + f_1 D)\, EDU + (g_0 + g_1 D)\, AGR + error \\ &= a_0 + a_1 D + b_0 GDP + b_1 (D{*}GDP) + c_0 POP + c_1 (D{*}POP) \\ &\quad + d_0 URB + d_1 (D{*}URB) + e_0 LIT + e_1 (D{*}LIT) + f_0 EDU \\ &\quad + f_1 (D{*}EDU) + g_0 AGR + g_1 (D{*}AGR) + error \end{aligned}$$

Call this Model D. We will generate all the interaction terms of the form D * variable.

b. $a_1 = b_1 = c_1 = d_1 = e_1 = f_1 = g_1 = 0.$

c. First regress Y against a constant, GDP, POP, URB, LIT, EDU, and AGR. This is the basic model (A). Next compute $\hat{u} = Y - \hat{a} - \hat{b}\,GDP - \hat{c}\,POP - \hat{d}\,URB - \hat{e}\,LIT - \hat{f}\,EDU - \hat{g}AGR$. Then regress $\hat{u}$ against all the right hand side variables in Model B above. This is the auxiliary regression.

d. Compute LM $= 40\,R^2$, where R^2 is the unadjusted R^2 in the auxiliary regression. Under the null hypothesis, LM has the Chi-square distribution with 7 d.f.

e. The critical value is $\text{LM}^* = 12.017$. The decision rule is to reject the null if $\text{LM} > 12.017$.

f. For the Wald approach, estimate the basic model A and save the error sum of squares as ESSA. Then estimate the general model B and save its error sum of squares as ESSB. Next compute

$$F_c = \frac{(\text{ESSA} - \text{ESSB})/7}{\text{ESSB}/(40 - 14)}$$

Under the null this has an F-distribution with d.f. 7 and 26. Look up the critical value F^* from the F-table corresponding to the level of significance and d.f. Reject the null if $F_c > F^*$.

EX 7.11

Suppose we exclude the years 1940 through 1945. The data used for estimation will be the 52 periods 1930-1939 and 1946-1987. Define $D = 1$ for the postwar period and 0 in the previous period. Assuming that $\alpha = \alpha_0 + \alpha_1 D$ and $\beta = \beta_0 + \beta_1 D$ we get the complete model $C = \alpha_0 + \alpha_1 D + \beta_0 Y + \beta_1 (DY) + u$. The relevant test is a Wald test on $\alpha_1 = \beta_1 = 0$.

EX 7.12

a. The β's are the marginal effect of income on expenditure on housing. The hypothesis states that this marginal effect is the same across the three age groups.

b. Define two dummy variables; $D_1 = 1$ if age is between 31 and 55, 0 otherwise, and $D_2 = 1$ if age is 56 or over. The unrestricted model is

$$E = a_0 + a_1 D_1 + a_2 D_2 + b_0 Y + b_1 D_1 Y + b_2 D_2 Y + u.$$

This is estimated by regressing E against a constant, D_1, D_2, Y, and the interaction terms $D_1 Y$ and $D_2 Y$. Under the specified hypothesis, $b_1 = b_2 = 0$. Impose this restriction and regress E against a constant, D_1, D_2, and Y. Next compute F_c by equation (4.3) with $m = 2$. Reject the null hypothesis if $F_c > F^*_{2,n-6}(a)$ which is the point on $F_{2,n-6}$ to the right of which the area is a.

EX 7.13

a. If there are more competing stations in the same area, a given station's market share will decrease. We can therefore expect $\dfrac{\partial SHARE}{\partial STAT}$ to be negative. If more households are wired for cable, the demand for a commercial television's programs is likely to decrease. Hence $\dfrac{\partial SHARE}{\partial CABLE} < 0$. An increase in income is likely to increase the overall demand for television but there is no reason to expect that a particular station's share will be affected. That is, $\dfrac{\partial SHARE}{\partial INCOME} = 0$.

b. Let $VHF = 1$ if the t-th station is VHF and 0 otherwise. Let $ABC = 1$ if the station is affiliated with ABC, and 0 otherwise. Similarly, let $CBS = 1$ for a CBS station and 0 otherwise. Let $NBC = 1$ for an NBC affiliated station. The control group consists of those not affiliated with ABC, NBC, or CBS.

(i) Let $\alpha = \alpha_0 + \alpha_1 UHF + \alpha_2 ABC + \alpha_3 CBS + \alpha_4 NBC$. The null hypothesis $\alpha_1 = \alpha_2 = \alpha_3 = \alpha_4 = 0$ is tested by a Wald F-test.

(ii) Let $\beta = \beta_0 + \beta_1 UHF + \cdots$, and similarly for γ and δ. The null hypothesis $\alpha_1 = \beta_1 = \gamma_1 = \delta_1 = \cdots = 0$ (excluding α_0, β_0, and δ_0) is tested by the Wald test.

EX 7.14

a. The null hypothesis is that the coefficient for DCAM is zero. The alternative is that it is not zero. The t-statistic for Model A is $t_c = -0.041/0.052 = -0.788$. Because $|t_c| < t^*_{417}(0.05)$, the coefficient is insignificant at the 10 percent level. The same result holds for Model D also.

b. The null hypothesis is that the coefficient for DPUB is zero and the alternative is that it is nonzero. For Model A, $t_c = 0.029/0.063 = 0.46$. This is also very small indicating insignificance.

c. The null hypothesis is that the coefficients for DSCI, DSOC, DHUM, and DARTS are all zero. The alternative is that at least one of the coefficients is nonzero. The unrestricted model is Model A. The restricted model is Model D. The test statistic is

$$F_c = \frac{(ESS_D - ESS_A)/4}{ESS_A/417} = 0.789$$

Under the null hypothesis, $F_c \sim F_{4,417}$. $F^*_{4,417}(0.1) = 1.94$ which is greater than F_c. We therefore accept the null hypothesis and conclude that the major does not matter in determining COLGPA. When Model B is the unrestricted model, Model C becomes the restricted model. $F_c = 0.807$ which is also insignificant.

d. We have,

$$F_c = \frac{(ESS_C - ESS_A)/6}{ESS_A/417} = 0.694$$

This too is insignificant. The conclusion is that none of the dummy variables have significant coefficients.

EX 7.15

Define new dummy variables, $PROF = 1$ for a professor, 0 for others, $ASSOC = 1$ for an associate professor, 0 for others (assistant professors being the control group), $OPP = 1$ if the opportunity for promotion is good, $SPOUSE = 1$ if the spouse has a good opportunity for employment, and $HAPPY = 1$ if the professor is happy with the administration.

a. The unrestricted model is

$$AVGYR = \alpha_0 + \alpha_1 ASSOC + \alpha_2 PROF + \alpha_3 OPP + \alpha_4 HAPPY + \alpha_5 SPOUSE + \beta PAPERS + \gamma AGE + u$$

The null hypothesis is $\alpha_1 = \alpha_2 = \alpha_3 = \alpha_4 = \alpha_5 = 0$ and the restricted model is

$$AVGYR = \alpha_0 + \beta PAPERS + \gamma AGE + u$$

The test is the Wald test using equation (4.3).

b. We write

$$\beta = \beta_0 + \beta_1 ASSOC + \cdots$$

$$\gamma = \gamma_0 + \gamma_1 ASSOC + \cdots$$

The null hypothesis is that $\alpha_i = \beta_i = \gamma_i = 0$ for $i = 1, 2, 3, 4, 5$. The usual Wald test is the appropriate one.

EX 7.16

To allow for the relationship $E_t = a + b\,T_t + u_t$ to be different across the time of day, define 23 hourly dummies; $H2 = 1$ for hour 2 (2:00 - 2:59 am), 0 otherwise, and similarly for other hours (hour 1 is the control and is ignored to avoid the dummy variable trap). First estimate the basic model above and save the residuals $\hat{u}_t$. Next regress $\hat{u}_t$ against a constant, $T_t, H2_t, H3_t$, ... , and $H24_t$ (this is the auxiliary regression). Compute LM = nR^2, where n is the number of observations and R^2 is the unadjusted R^2 from the auxiliary regression. Reject the null hypothesis that the coefficients for Hi (i = 2, 3, ..., 24) are all zero if LM > LM* the point on χ^2_{23} with an area to the right equal to the level of significance. Alternatively, compute p-value = $P(\chi^2_{23} > \text{LM})$ and reject the null if it is less than the level of significance.

EX 7.17

a. H_0: $\beta_6 = \beta_7 = \beta_8 = \beta_9 = \beta_{10} = 0$.

b. Model A is the unrestricted model and Model B is the restricted model. Compute

$$F_c = \frac{(ESSB - ESSA)/5}{ESSA/(116 - 10)} = \frac{(5172.56 - 763.029)/5}{763.029/106} = 122.51$$

Under $H_0, F_c \sim F_{5,106}$.

c. From the F-table for 1 percent level, $F^*_{5,106}(0.01)$ is between 3.17 and 3.34. Since $F_c > F^*$, we reject H_0 and conclude that there has been a significant change in the structure.

d. Six out of the eight model selection criteria choose Model C as the best. But Model C has β_2 and β_8 with p-values slightly above 10 percent. Omitted variable bias suggests that it is better to leave a variable in a model if it appears to have some effect. Since β_2 and β_8 are only slightly insignificant, Model C is the best.

e.

	1980	1990
Famsize	4.944	4.944 + 9.760 = 14.704
Highschl	0.223	0.223 + 0.199 = 0.422
College	0.339	0.339 + 0.871 = 1.210

f. In 1990 an increase in family size of one person resulted in an average increase of $14,704 in median income. This is $9,760 more than the same marginal effect in 1980.

A one percent increase in high school graduates increased median income on average by $422 in 1990, which is $199 more than the marginal effect in 1980.

A one percent increase in college graduates increased median income on average by $422 in 1990, which is $199 more than the marginal effect in 1980.

EX 7.18

a. The larger the population the greater the number of cars, buses, planes, and other transportation equipment that cause air pollution. Value added is an indicator of economic activity and hence can be expected to contribute to air pollution. Rain usually clears the air and hence can be expected to improve air quality. Population density would have the same effect as population. Median income is also an indicator of economic activity that often worsens air quality. The poverty level of an SMSA is not likely to affect air quality. ELECTR, FUELOIL, INDESTAB, are all indicators of economic activity. We would expect them to contribute adversely to air quality.

b.

$$
\begin{aligned}
AIRQUAL = \beta_0 + \beta_1 VALADD + \beta_2 RAIN + \beta_3 DENSITY \\
+ \beta_4 MEDINCM + \beta_5 ELECTR \\
+ \beta_6 FUELOIL + \beta_7 INESTAB + u
\end{aligned}
$$

Population is excluded because the density of population is included. Poverty rate is excluded because it does not appear to be relevant. The estimated model is (t-statistics in parenthesis)

$$\hat{AIRQUAL} = \underset{(4.84)}{97.160} + \underset{(0.50)}{0.002}VALADD - \underset{(-0.07)}{0.032}\,RAIN$$

$$- \underset{(-0.36)}{0.000748}\,DENSITY - \underset{(-0.04)}{0.000104}\,MEDINCM$$

$$+ \underset{(0.27)}{0.052}\,ELECR + \underset{(0.54)}{0.000946}\,FUELOIL$$

$$- \underset{(-0.05)}{0.001}\,INDESTAB$$

$$R^2 = 0.138 \quad \bar{R}^2 = -0.136 \quad F = 0.505 \quad d.f. = 22$$

The negative value for $\bar{R}^2$ indicates a poor model. It can be verified that the low F-statistic indicates that the overall significance of the model is very poor.

c. Yes, we would expect multicollinearity problems. For instance, the correlation between INDESTAB and MEDINC is 0.986 which is almost perfect. The correlation between INDESTAB and VALADD is 0.921. As we know from Chapter 6, multicollinearity lowers t-statistics and is likely to make regression coefficients insignificant. This certainly appears to be the case here.

d. For simplicity, we assume that only the constant is affected by the dummy variable COAST. Coastal SMSA's frequently have winds from ofF-shore which clear up air pollution. We might therefore expect a negative coefficient for COAST. Empirically this result holds with a strong t-statistic.

e. By eliminating insignificant variables in a step by step fashion, the "final model" was obtained as follows:

$$\hat{AIRQUAL} = \underset{(15.7)}{122.258} + \underset{(2.4)}{0.0026}\,FUELOIL - \underset{(-3.6)}{33.497}\,COAST$$

$$\bar{R}^2 = 0.324 \qquad F = 7.963 \qquad d.f. = 27$$

The F-statistic is significant at the level 0.0019 and $\bar{R}^2$ is positive. It is interesting to note that all the economic activity variables thought to be important a priori are empirically insignificant. Air quality depends mainly on the amount of fuel oil used and whether an SMSA is on the coast or not.

f. A number of transportation variables could be entered directly; numbers of automobiles, trucks, and planes; number of gallons of gasoline consumed. Another variable is the number of tons of solid waste burned in sewage plants and solid waste incinerators.

EX 7.19

Use the following ESL commands to obtain the results necessary to answer this question.

```
genr lsqft = log(sqft)
ols price const sqft lsqft yard ;
(* compute the marginal effect of sqft on price *)
genr DPDSQFT = coeff(sqft) + (coeff(lsqft)/sqft)
graph DPDSQFT sqft ;
(* kitchen sink model with all the characteristics of a home *)
ols price const sqft lsqft yard age aircon baths bedrms cond corner
 culd dish fence firepl floors garage irreg lajolla lndry patio pool
 rooms sprink view ;
(* omit variables with high p-values *)
omit age aircon bedrms cond corner dish floors garage patio ;
omit culd fence ;
omit rooms ;
omit lndry pool ;
```

The basic model does not have a good fit because it explains only 45.5 percent of the variation in the price of homes. The regression coefficients are all significant at levels below 1.5 percent. The marginal effect of SQFT on PRICE is given by

$$\frac{\Delta \widehat{PRICE}}{\Delta SQFT} = \hat{\beta} + \frac{\hat{\gamma}}{SQFT} = 0.34218 - \frac{501.64495}{SQFT}$$

The graph of this relationship (see the output file *ex6-12.out*) indicates that the marginal effect is negative at low values of SQFT, but increases steadily as SQFT increases. This is counterintuitive and might be because the marginal effect holds other variables constant which is not realistic. For instance, the size of the yard is not the same between a home with SQFT 950 and another with SQFT 3,500.

The complete model explains about 70 percent of the variation in price. However, many of the regression coefficients have very high *p*-values indicating insignificance. After omitting these, a few at a time, the "final" model explains about 76.8 percent of the variation in price. The significance of the variables are as follows, and all have expected signs:

1 percent : SQFT, LSQFT, LA JOLLA
1-5 percent : YARD, IRREG, SPRINK
5-10 percent : BATHS, FIREPL, VIEW, LNDRY, POOL

EX 7.20

Listed below are the ESL commands required for the empirical analysis. It will be noted that this is more involved than the previous exercises, first because of the LM test and second because the test for unitary elasticity requires covariances.

```
(* Generate logs for the double-log model *)
logs Q Y P ED1 ED2 ;
(* Estimate basic model *)
ols l_Q const l_Y l_P l_ED1 l_ED2 ;
(* Save residuals *)
genr ut = uhat
(* Generate interaction terms *)
genr D82l_Y = D82*l_Y
genr D86l_Y = D86*l_Y
genr D82l_P = D82*l_P
genr D86l_P = D86*l_P
genr D82l_ED1 = D82*l_ED1
genr D86l_ED1 = D86*l_ED1
genr D82l_ED2 = D82*l_ED2
genr D86l_ED2 = D86*l_ED2
(* The following did not work because of exact multicollinearity *)
ols ut const l_Y l_P l_ED1 l_ED2 D82 D86 D82l_Y D86l_Y D82l_P
   D86l_P D82l_ED1 D86l_ED1 D82l_ED2 D86l_ED2 ;
(* Verify from correlation matrix that there is exact multicollinearity *)
corr l_Y l_P l_ED1 l_ED2 D82 D86 D82l_Y D86l_Y D82l_P D86l_P
   D82l_ED1 D86l_ED1 D82l_ED2 D86l_ED2 ;
(* Estimate a smaller auxiliary regression *)
ols ut const l_Y l_P l_ED1 l_ED2 D82 D86 D82l_Y D82l_P D86l_P
   D82l_ED1 D82l_ED2 ;
(* Compute LM test statistic *)
genr LM = $nrsq
```

```
(* Compute p-value *)
p-value 3 7 LM
(* Estimate general model and then omit variables *)
ols l_Q const l_Y l_P l_ED1 l_ED2 D82 D86 D82l_Y D82l_P D86l_P
 D82l_ED1 D82l_ED2 ;
omit D86l_P ;
omit D82l_ED2 ;
omit l_ED1 ;
omit l_ED2 ;
omit D86 ;
omit D82l_Y ;
(* Obtain covariance matrix of coefficients for final model *)
ols -o l_Q const l_Y l_P D82 D82l_Y D82l_P D82l_ED1 ;
```

An LM test could not be performed against the most general model as the alternative because many of the interaction terms were perfectly correlated (for example, D86 and D86*ln Y). The LM test statistic for a smaller alternative was 23.762, with a d.f. of 7 and a *p*-value of 0.001254. This indicates that many of the interaction terms are worth including. In this example, the "simple to general" LM test approach and the "general to simple" Hendry/LSE approach both give the same results. The regression coefficients and associated statistics for the final model (chosen to have the lowest selection criteria) are given below.

```
-----------------------------------------------------------------------
VARIABLE          COEFFICIENT         STDERROR        T STAT       PROB t > |T|

constant            -4.996884         0.499668     -10.00041      < 0.0001 ***
l_Y                  0.731728         0.067115      10.902559     < 0.0001 ***
l_P                 -0.370761         0.095249      -3.892553     0.000784 ***
D82                -18.918957        10.844478      -1.74457      0.095016 *
D82l_Y               1.804299         1.164538       1.549368      0.13556
D82l_P               0.638396         0.148028       4.312682     0.000281 ***
D82l_ED1            -2.937286         0.945721      -3.10587      0.005154 ***

Unadjusted R-squared    0.940       Adjusted R-squared              0.924

COVARIANCE MATRIX OF REGRESSION COEFFICIENTS

    10) l_Y      11) l_P        7) D82     15) D82l_Y     17) D82l_P

   0.004504    -0.005795      0.033494     -0.004504      0.005795   (10
                0.009072     -0.042124      0.005795     -0.009072   (11
-----------------------------------------------------------------------
```

```
---------------------------------------------------------------------------
     10) l_Y        11) l_P         7) D82     15) D821_Y     17) D821_P

                                117.602712     -12.622348     -0.294506   (7
                                                 1.356149      0.026816   (15
                                                               0.021912   (17
   19) D821_ED1        0) const
   3.050952e-14      -0.033494    (10
  -4.679141e-14       0.042124    (11
       9.973193      -0.249668    (7
      -1.062523       0.033494    (15
      -0.048404      -0.042124    (17
       0.894388 -2.224446e-13     (19
                      0.249668    (0
---------------------------------------------------------------------------
```

The first thing to note is that the dummy variable for 1986 onward and all its interactions have dropped out. This is not surprising because D86 was 1 only for three periods which are not enough to identify significant shifts. Also, the shift in income elasticity in 1982-1988 is weak with a p-value as high as 0.13556. But omission of this variable made six of the eight selection criteria worse and so we have retained it. The final model explains 92.4 percent of the variance in the log of the cigarette demand. The dummy variable D82 that shifts the constant term is significantly negative indicating that there has been an appreciable drop in overall cigarette demand due to the 1981 health warning. Similarly, the effect of education was also to reduce the demand significantly. The price and income elasticities for the two time periods are given below.

1960-81 income elasticity	0.731728
1982-88 income elasticity	2.536027 (= 0.731728 + 1.804299)
1960-81 price elasticity	– 0.370761
1982-88 price elasticity	0.267635 (= – 0.370761 + 0.638396)

The positive sign of the price elasticity in 1982-88 is surprising and it is not clear why this is so in Turkey. Similarly, the high income elasticity in the same period is hard to understand. To test whether the price and income elasticities for 1960-81 are equal to 1, the test statistics are

Income elasticity	$(1 - 0.731728) / 0.067115 = 3.997$
Price elasticity	$(1 - 0.370761) / 0.095249 = 6.606$

Under the null hypothesis of unitary elasticity, this has a t-distribution with 22 d.f. From the t-table on the inside front cover, we readily note that these are quite significant at levels below 0.001. Thus we conclude that these elasticities are not unitary. For the 1981-88 period, the elasticities are the sums of two regression coefficients. Therefore the test involves a linear combination of coefficients of the form $\beta_1 + \beta_2 = 1$. The most straightforward method is the direct t-test described in Section 4.4. The test statistic is

$$t_c = \frac{\hat{\beta}_1 + \hat{\beta}_2 - 1}{\hat{Var}(\hat{\beta}_1) + \hat{Var}(\hat{\beta}_2) + 2\hat{Cov}(\hat{\beta}_1, \hat{\beta}_2)}$$

For the two elasticities we have (the variances are the diagonal elements and the covariances are the off-diagonal elements in the above table)

$$\text{Income elasticity} \quad t_c = \frac{0.731728 + 1.804299 - 1}{0.004504 + 1.356149 - 0.004504} = 1.133$$

$$\text{Price elasticity} \quad t_c = \frac{-0.370761 + 0.638396 - 1}{0.009072 + 0.021912 - 0.009072} = -33.42$$

It is evident from the test statistics that we can reject the hypothesis of unitary elasticity in the case of price but not in the case of income.

EX 7.21

To obtain the empirical results for this question, use the following ESL commands.

```
(* First generate all the interactions with the dummy variable soc *)
genr socgnp = soc*gnp
genr socgdp = soc*gdp
genr socpop = soc*pop
genr socurb = soc*urb
genr soclit = soc*lit
genr socedu = soc*edu
genr socagr = soc*agr
list
(* Estimate a general model. Most general model cannot be estimated
because of exact multicollinearity *)
ols Y const gnp gdp pop urb lit edu agr soc socgnp socgdp socpop
 socurb ;
(* omit variables one at a time *)
omit lit ;
```

```
omit gdp ;
omit urb ;
omit socpop ;
omit socurb ;
omit socgdp ;
omit soc ;
```

The final model estimates are given below.

VARIABLE	COEFFICIENT	STDERROR	T STAT	2Prob(t > |T|)	
constant	0.509996	0.067566	7.54813	< 0.0001	***
gnp	-4.092969e-05	2.376095e-05	-1.722561	0.094054	*
pop	0.037434	0.016057	2.331296	0.025802	**
edu	-0.001798	9.874280e-04	-1.820717	0.077461	*
agr	-0.002532	9.583435e-04	-2.641539	0.012381	**
socgnp	-1.686402e-04	5.664833e-05	-2.976967	0.005333	***

Unadjusted R-squared 0.678 Adjusted R-squared 0.631

According to the selection criteria, the best model was the one which had the variables gnp, pop, edu, agr, and socgnp. The model explains 63.1 percent of the variance of the Gini coefficient. A country with a higher per capita gnp had, on average, a lower gini coefficient, that is, a better equality. Other things being equal, larger countries had larger inequality, on average. Education had a negative effect. Agrarian economies tend to have, on average, lower gini coefficients or better equality of income distribution. The same is true of Socialist countries.

EX 7.22

Use the following ESL commands to obtain the empirical results.

```
(* Estimate basic model and save residuals as ut and d.f. as dfr *)
ols grth const y60 inv school pop ;
genr ut=uhat
genr dfr=$df
(* generate all the interaction terms with the dummy variables *)
genr dny60 = dn*y60
genr dninv=dn*inv
genr dnpop=dn*pop
genr dnschl=dn*school
genr diy60 = di*y60
```

```
genr diinv=di*inv
genr dipop=di*pop
genr dischl=di*school
genr oecdy60 = doecd*y60
genr oecdinv=doecd*inv
genr oecdpop=doecd*pop
genr oecdschl=doecd*school
list
(* Estimate the auxiliary regression for the LM test for adding dummy
variables and their interactions *)
ols ut const y60 inv pop school dn di doecd dny60 dninv dnpop dnschl
 diy60 diinv dipop dischl oecdy60 oecdinv oecdpop oecdschl ;
(*  Compute the LM test statistic and the number of restrictions *)
genr dfu=$df
genr NR = dfr-dfu
genr LM = $nrsq
(*  Compute p-value for LM *)
pvalue 3 15 LM
(* From the auxiliary regression choose new variables with p-values less
than 0.5 and add to basic model *)
ols grth const y60 inv pop school dn di doecd dnpop dnschl diy60
 diinv dipop dischl oecdpop ;
(* omit variables with insignificant coefficients, one at a time *)
omit diinv ;
omit dnpop ;
omit pop ;
omit diy60 ;
omit dipop ;
omit di ;
omit school ;
omit dnschl ;
omit doecd ;
(* Starting with the most general model use data-based model reduction *)
ols grth const y60 inv pop school dn di doecd dny60 dninv dnpop
 dnschl diy60 diinv dipop dischl oecdy60 oecdinv oecdpop oecdschl ;
omit oecdy60 ;
omit dny60 ;
```

omit oecdschl ;
omit diy60 ;
omit diinv ;
omit oecdinv ;
omit dipop ;
omit di ;
omit dn ;
omit dnpop ;
omit pop ;
omit school ;
omit dnschl ;
omit doecd ;

The estimated best models using the two approaches are given below.

FINAL MODEL USING THE SIMPLE TO GENERAL APPROACH AND THE LM TEST

VARIABLE	COEFFICIENT	STDERROR	T STAT	2Prob(t > |T|)
constant	2.644787	0.466134	5.673881	< 0.0001 ***
y60	-0.419989	0.048383	-8.680544	< 0.0001 ***
inv	0.497214	0.077031	6.454747	< 0.0001 ***
dn	-0.838338	0.156478	-5.357548	< 0.0001 ***
dischl	0.314639	0.051152	6.151018	< 0.0001 ***
oecdpop	-0.09824	0.033699	-2.915242	0.004405 ***

Unadjusted R-squared 0.628 Adjusted R-squared 0.609

MODEL SELECTION STATISTICS

SGMASQ	0.08906	AIC	0.094186	FPE	0.094198
HQ	0.100191	SCHWARZ	0.109709	SHIBATA	0.093605
GCV	0.094513	RICE	0.094868		

FINAL MODEL USING THE GENERAL TO SIMPLE APPROACH

VARIABLE	COEFFICIENT	STDERROR	T STAT	2Prob(t > |T|)
constant	1.749406	0.365041	4.792351	< 0.0001 ***
y60	-0.408027	0.047102	-8.662631	< 0.0001 ***
inv	0.793348	0.087186	9.099484	< 0.0001 ***
dninv	-0.305886	0.056535	-5.410592	< 0.0001 ***
dischl	0.310223	0.050511	6.141729	< 0.0001 ***
oecdpop	-0.096118	0.033538	-2.86599	0.005088 ***

Unadjusted R-squared 0.630 Adjusted R-squared 0.611

```
--------------------------------------------------------------------------
MODEL SELECTION STATISTICS

SGMASQ       0.088661     AIC        0.093764     FPE          0.093776
HQ           0.099742     SCHWARZ    0.109217     SHIBATA      0.093185
GCV          0.094089     RICE       0.094443
--------------------------------------------------------------------------
```

Note that the final models using the two approaches are not the same. In terms of model selection statistics, the general to simple approach had the best model. There is a negative effect on growth in income due to the level of income, indicating a diminishing marginal effect. The marginal effect of investment was $\partial \widehat{grth}/\partial inv$ = 0.793348 - 0.305886 dn, which gives the value 0.793348 for an oil-producing country and 0.487462 for a non-oil-producing country. Schooling has the expected positive effect but mattered only for an industrialized country. Population had a negative effect but only for OECD countries.

EX 7.23

ESL commands that would be useful in answering this question are too numerous to list here. The disk available from the author has the detail commands.

The final model has adjusted R^2 of 0.221, slightly more than all the models in Exercise 7.14. The variables remaining that have significant coefficients are hsgpa, msat, dsoc, hsgpa*public, vsat*pub, and msat*dsoc. High school GPA is a good predictor of college GPA and so is the SAT score for mathematics. Public schools interact with high school GPA and the verbal SAT score. Surprisingly, only Sociology majors differ significantly compared to the control group which is undeclared major.

EX 7.24

Use the following ESL commands to obtain the results for this. First generate interaction terms with the dummy variable.

```
(* First generate interaction terms with the dummy variable. *)
genr durb=D90*urb
genr dfamsize=D90*famsize
genr dunemp=D90*unemp
genr dhighsch=D90*highschl
genr dcollege=D90*college
list
```

```
(* Estimate most general model with all the shifts *)
ols povrate const urb famsize unemp highschl college D90 durb dfamsize
 dunemp dhighsch dcollege ;
(* omit variables one at a time *)
omit urb ;
omit D90 ;
omit dhighsch ;
omit dunemp ;
```

The estimated final model is given below.

VARIABLE	COEFFICIENT	STDERROR	T STAT	2Prob(t > |T|)	
constant	39.230373	6.959222	5.637178	< 0.0001	***
famsize	-3.578732	1.362769	-2.626074	0.009892	***
unemp	0.125908	0.075744	1.662296	0.099353	*
highschl	-0.298614	0.051984	-5.744348	< 0.0001	***
college	-0.199581	0.046609	-4.282046	< 0.0001	***
durb	-0.038509	0.017259	-2.231287	0.027728	**
dfamsize	1.922828	0.52315	3.67548	0.000371	***
dcollege	-0.206024	0.062358	-3.303895	0.001294	***

Unadjusted R-squared 0.611 Adjusted R-squared 0.586

Since several of the dummy variable terms are very significant, it is clear that there has been a structural change. The estimated models for the two periods are given below (verify them).

1980 Census: $\widehat{povrate} = 39.230373 - 3.578732\ famsize + 0.125908\ unemp - 0.298614\ highschl - 0.199581\ college$

1990 Census: $\widehat{povrate} = 39.230373 - 1.655904\ famsize + 0.125908\ unemp - 0.298614\ highschl - 0.405605\ college - 0.038509\ urb$

Note that there is a substantial difference in the effects of family size on poverty rates with a smaller numerical impact in 1990 compared to 1980. There is a similar large difference in the effects of college education. In 1990 a one percent increase in college education, holding other variables constant, decreased poverty rates much more drastically than in 1980.

EX 7.25

The ESL commands needed to obtain the empirical results are very extensive because both the simple to general and the general to simple approaches are used here.

```
genr lsalary=ln(salary)
(* generate interaction terms *)
genr d1years=d1*years
genr d2years=d2*years
genr d3years=d3*years
genr d4years=d4*years
genr d5years=d5*years
genr d6years=d6*years
(* estimate the most general model with all shifts *)
ols lsalary const d1 d2 d3 d4 d5 d6 years d1years d2years d3years
 d4years d5years ;
(* retrieve ESS and d.f. for the Wald test *)
genr ESSU=$ess
genr DFU=$df
(* omit variables one at a time *)
omit d5 ;
omit d4years ;
omit d4 ;
omit d2years ;
omit d2 ;
omit d1years ;
omit d3 ;
omit d5years ;
(* final model using the general to simple approach *)
omit d1 ;
(* estimate the basic model *)
ols lsalary const years ;
(* retrieve ESS and d.f. for the Wald test *)
genr ESSR=$ess
genr DFR=$df
(* calculate the number of restrictions *)
genr NR=DFR-DFU
```

```
genr ut=uhat
(* Calculate F-statistic and its pvalue for the Wald test *)
genr Fc=(ESSR-ESSU)*DFU/(ESSU*NR)
pvalue 4 11 209 Fc
(* auxiliary regression for the LM test *)
ols ut const d1 d2 d3 d4 d5 d6 years d1years d2years d3years d4years
 d5years ;
genr LM=$nrsq
pvalue 3 11 LM
(* estimate model after selecting new variables with pvalues < 0.5 *)
ols lsalary const d1 d2 d3 d4 d6 years d1years d2years d3years d4years ;
(* omit variables one at a time *)
omit d4 ;
omit d4years ;
omit d2years ;
omit d2 ;
omit d1years ;
omit d3 ;
(* final model for simple to general approach is the same as before *)
omit d1 ;
```

Even though there were seven universities involved, seven dummy variables were not used because we would have exact multicollinearity (note the discussion on the dummy variable trap).

Both the LM and Wald tests strongly support the hypothesis that the relationship between log salary and years since Ph.D. is different across universities. Also, the simple to general approach and the general to simple approach both yield the same final model whose estimates are reproduced below.

VARIABLE	COEFFICIENT	STDERROR	T STAT	2Prob(t > |T|)
constant	3.956204	0.028455	139.032986	< 0.0001 ***
d6	0.100503	0.039191	2.564433	0.011006 **
years	0.020323	0.00141	14.416053	< 0.0001 ***
d3years	-0.004337	0.001801	-2.408233	0.016862 **
Unadjusted R-squared	0.514	Adjusted R-squared		0.507

In terms of model selection statistics and goodness of fit the final model is clearly superior to the basic model which had no shifts in the intercept or slope terms due to universities. Not surprisingly, here also the number of years of experience matters in determining the salary patterns but only one university had a significantly different slope term and another university had a significantly different intercept term. Otherwise, the universities were alike in behavior.

EX 7.26

Use the following ESL commands to reproduce the results here.

```
genr time
genr d1time=d1*time
genr d2time=d2*time
ols POP 0 d1 d2 time d1time d2time ;
genr pophat=POP-uhat
graph pophat POP YEAR ;
```

As expected, the structures are very different in the three periods. The estimated model with complete structural shifts is given below along with the graphs for the observed and fitted values on the next page. Note that the new model tracks the population trend extremely well.

VARIABLE	COEFFICIENT	STDERROR	T STAT	2Prob(t > |T|)
constant	53.197455	0.051415	1034.673302	< 0.0001 ***
d1	2.742709	0.171019	16.037477	< 0.0001 ***
d2	-1.113873	0.230255	-4.837554	< 0.0001 ***
time	0.269815	0.006986	38.622824	< 0.0001 ***
d1time	-0.251178	0.01155	-21.747748	< 0.0001 ***
d2time	-0.079524	0.010595	-7.506051	< 0.0001 ***

Unadjusted R-squared 0.996 Adjusted R-squared 0.995

EX 7.27

Use the following ESL commands for this exercise.

```
ols price const hatch wbase length width height weight cyl liters
 gasmpg trans ;
omit width liters ;
omit trans ;
omit wbase ;
omit gasmpg ;
```

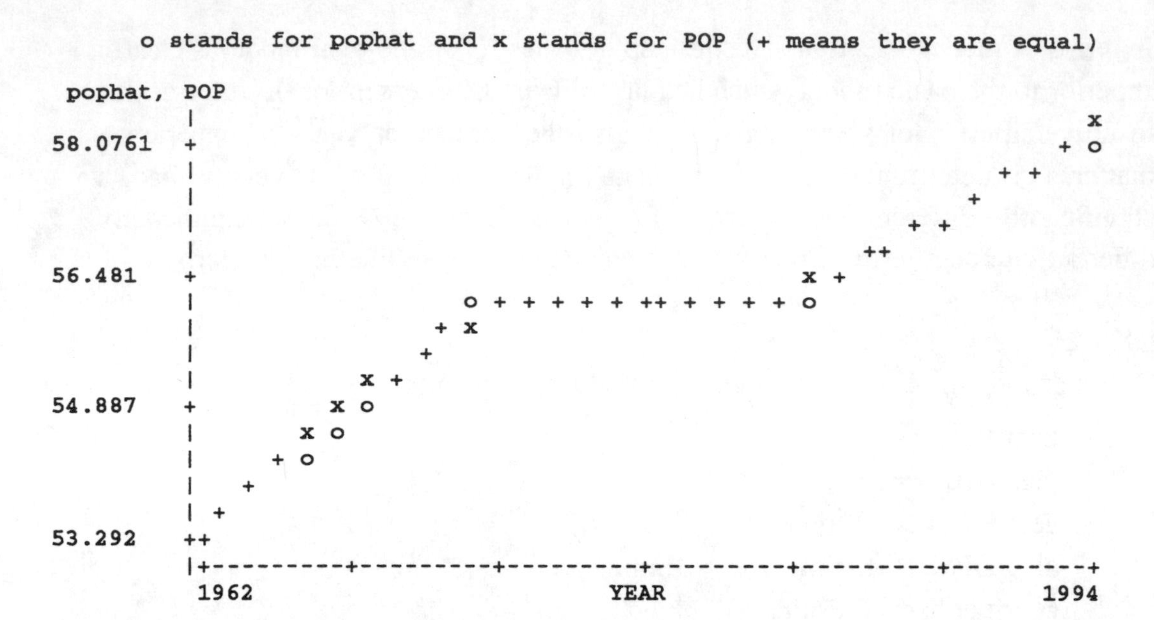

The estimated final model for Exercise 7.27 is given below.

VARIABLE	COEFFICIENT	STDERROR	T STAT	2Prob(t > |T|)	
constant	105.590881	26.80301	3.939516	0.00018	***
hatch	-3.932124	1.78947	-2.197369	0.031041	**
length	-0.508133	0.125807	-4.038975	0.000127	***
height	-1.144366	0.46269	-2.473291	0.01562	**
weight	2.10477	0.363424	5.7915	< 0.0001	***
cyl	1.198361	0.674012	1.777951	0.079412	*
Unadjusted R-squared		0.621	Adjusted R-squared	0.596	

We would expect a hatch back to sell for a lower price than a sedan and the estimated regression agrees with this prior notion. Similarly, increasing the weight or the number of cylinders is likely to increase the list price of a car and that is the case here also. However, the coefficients for length and height are negative and counterintuitive. A possible explanation is the high correlation among the explanatory variables, for example, between length and weight.

EX 7.28

Because the ESL commands are too numerous they are not included here. The final model with the best model selection statistics is given below.

VARIABLE	COEFFICIENT	STDERROR	T STAT	2Prob(t > |T|)
constant	8.259541	8.866585	0.931536	0.353913
homes	0.541761	0.061444	8.817172	< 0.0001 ***
D	17.998683	11.492005	1.566192	0.120594
sq_tvcha	-0.335532	0.125358	-2.676596	0.008747 ***
dsqhome	-2.636982e-04	5.956758e-05	-4.426875	< 0.0001 ***
Unadjusted R-squared	0.711	Adjusted R-squared		0.699

Although the dummy variable D had an insignificant coefficient with a *p*-value of 12 percent, it is retained because the model selection statistics are the best for this model and it is safer to keep a variable in the model rather than face the omitted variable bias. The number of homes and the number of tv signals have nonlinear effects. For homes, the effect initially increases and then decreases. This suggests a diminishing marginal effect for the size of the population.

EX 7.29

The ESL commands for obtaining the empirical results are as follows.

```
ols hr const exec unemp nwr south capleg y ;
omit exec ;
omit capleg ;
```

Six of the eight model selection criteria choose the second model as the "best". The coefficient for the legality of capital punishment is positive and counterintuitive. However, it is significant only at the 15 percent level, which is unexpectedly high. Thus, other things being equal, the legality of capital punishment in a state does not significantly reduce the homicide rate.

EX 7.30

The ESL commands for obtaining the empirical results are as follows.

```
ols pvote const pvote86 pvote84 vbush terms amtinc amtchall resource
 lcvrate demo ;
omit vbush lcvrate ;
omit resource ;
omit pvote84 ;
omit terms ;
omit amtinc ;
```

omit demo ;

The last model was the best in terms of the selection criteria. That model explains only 50 percent of the variation in the proportion of votes in 1988. Also, the only significant variables were the proportion of votes in 1986 (positive effect) and the amount spent by the challenger (negative, as expected).

EX 7.31

The following ESL commands would be useful in obtaining the empirical results.

```
ols appl const founded applfee tuition room R&D pp satv satm ;
omit satv ;
omit R&D ;
omit founded ;
omit satm ;
omit tuition ;
```

The last model was the best in terms of the selection criteria. That model explains only 42.5 percent of the variation in the number of applicants to college. The variables that remained in the model and significantly affected enrollments are the application fee (which counterintuitively had a positive effect), the cost of room and board (expected negative effect), and whether or not the school was private (expected negative effect). The year the school was founded, the tuition fee, R&D expenses, and the SAT score measures had no significant effects on applications.

EX 7.32

Output obtained with the following ESL commands will be useful for answering this question.

```
ols pop const educexp recexp policexp vcrime othrcrim unemprt city
 inland central south ;
(* violent crime is excluded because it does not make sense to have a
positive sign for it *)
ols pop const educexp recexp policexp othrcrim unemprt city inland
 central south ;
(* omit variables one at a time *)
omit central ;
omit othrcrim ;
```

omit unemprt ;
omit policexp ;
omit educexp ;

The estimated final model is given below.

VARIABLE	COEFFICIENT	STDERROR	T STAT	2Prob(t > |T|)	
constant	-934.942668	308.788246	-3.027779	0.003799	***
recexp	1.407273	0.22592	6.22908	< 0.0001	***
city	701.067755	236.401536	2.96558	0.004522	***
inland	512.835335	282.501057	1.81534	0.075131	*
south	1427.308784	350.552382	4.071599	0.000157	***

Unadjusted R-squared 0.666 Adjusted R-squared 0.641

As expected, recreation expenditures were very significant. Similarly, city and south dummy variables had positive signs which are also expected. However, the positive sign for the inland dummy is counterintuitive.

EX 7.33

Listed below are the ESL commands for this exercise.

genr LSALARY = ln(SALARY)
ols LSALARY const YRS HT WT AGE GAMES GAMESTRT
FORWARD GUARD MIN FGA FGPRCNT FTA FTPRCNT
REBOUNDS ASSISTS STEALS BLOCKS POINTS AVGPNTS
RACE EW TRD WINTM ALLSTAR XPAN ;
omit WT BLOCKS WINTM ;
omit HT ;
omit RACE ;
omit STEALS ;
omit MIN ;
omit GAMES ;
omit ASSISTS ;
omit FTA ;
omit POINTS ;
omit EW ;
omit TRD ;
omit FTPRCNT ;
omit FGPRCNT ;

```
omit GAMESTRT ;
omit YRS ;
omit AGE ;
omit REBOUNDS ;
omit XPAN ;
```

In spite of the presence of so many variables, the full model explains only 30.3 percent of the variance in the log of salary. In terms of the model selection statistics, the last but one model is the best. The remaining variables with the significant coefficients are FORWARD, GUARD, FGA, AVGPOINTS, ALLSTAR, and XPAN. The final model explains 35.8 percent of the variance of ln(SALARY).

EX 7.34

Use the following ESL commands to obtain the empirical results for this exercise.

```
ols UCOMP const UHOURS HEADY SPOUSEY EDUC MALE
   MARRIED FAMSIZE WHITE ;
omit SPOUSEY ;
```

Only one variable, SPOUSEY, had an insignificant coefficient and when it was eliminated all the remaining coefficients were significant at levels below 2 percent. The overall $\bar{R}^2$ is 0.521. The variables UHOURS, HEADY, EDUC, MALE, FAMSIZE, and WHITE had the expected positive coefficients. Only the variable MARRIED had a negative coefficient, which is counterintuitive.

CHAPTER 8

EXERCISES

EX 8.2

a. The density function for u_t is $\frac{1}{\sigma\sqrt{2\pi}} e^{-u_t^2/(2\sigma_t^2)}$. The likelihood function is therefore

$$L = \frac{1}{\sigma^n (2\pi)^{n/2}} e^{-\Sigma u_t^2/(2\sigma_t^2)}$$

Logarithm of this gives

$$\ln L = -n \ln \sigma - n \ln(\sqrt{2\pi}) - \sum \frac{u_t^2}{2\sigma_t^2}$$

Substituting for u_t from the model we get the desired answer.

b. When $\sigma_t^2 = \sigma^2 Z_t^2$, the log likelihood function becomes

$$\ln L = -n \ln \sigma - n \ln(\sqrt{2\pi}) - \sum \left[\frac{(Y_t - \beta_1 - \beta_2 X_{t1} - \beta_3 X_{t2})^2}{2\sigma^2 Z_t^2} \right]$$

Maximizing $\ln L$ is equivalent to minimizing

$$\Sigma \left[\frac{Y_t - \beta_1 - \beta_2 X_{t2} - \beta_3 X_{t3}}{Z_t} \right]^2 = \Sigma(w_t Y_t - \beta_1 w_t - \beta_2 w_t X_{t2} - \beta_3 w_t X_{t3})^2$$

where $w_t = 1/Z_t$. This gives the WLS estimates of Exercise 8.1.

EX 8.4

It is known that $\sigma_t^2 = \sigma^2 Z_t$. The weight for WLS is inversely proportional to the standard deviation of the error terms. Therefore $w_t = 1/\sqrt{Z_t}$. Multiply each variable by w_t and use the transformed variables in the regression.

EX 8.5

Divide both sides of the equation $Y_t = \beta_1 + \beta_2 X_t + \beta_3 X_t^2 + u_t$ by X_t. We get

$$\frac{Y_t}{X_t} = \beta_1 \frac{1}{X_t} + \beta_2 + \beta_3 X_t + \frac{u_t}{X_t}$$

It is easily verified that the variance of the error term, $\text{Var}(u_t / X_t)$, is a constant and hence the transformed model has homoscedasticity. Thus OLS on this model will give estimates that are BLUE. The procedure is therefore to regress Y_t / X_t against a constant, $1/X_t$, and X_t. Note that the estimate of the constant term is for β_2 and *not* for β_1.

EX 8.6

Let $w_t = 1/\sqrt{(1/n_t)} = \sqrt{n_t}$. Then the transformed model is $w_t Y_t = \beta_1 w_t + \beta_2 w_t X_{t2} + \beta_3 w_t X_{t3} + w_t u_t$. $\text{Var}(w_t u_t) = w_t^2 \text{Var}(u_t) = 1$. Therefore OLS applied to the transformed model will give estimates that are BLUE. Thus, we would regress $w_t Y_t$ against w_t, $w_t X_{t2}$, and $w_t X_{t3}$, with no constant term.

EX 8.7

Taking logarithm of both sides of the given condition that $\sigma_t^2 = \alpha P_t^\beta$, we get $\ln(\sigma_t^2) = \ln\alpha + \beta \ln P_t$. The null hypothesis is $\beta = 0$ and the alternative is that it is not zero. The auxiliary equation in this case is $\ln(\sigma_t^2) = \ln\alpha + \beta \ln P_t$. To compute the test statistic, (1) regress E_t against a constant and Y_t, (2) save the residual $\hat{u}_t = E_t - \hat{\beta}_1 - \hat{\beta}_2 Y_t$, (3) regress $\ln(\hat{u}_t^2)$ against a constant and $\ln(P_t)$, and (4) compute $\text{LM} = nR^2$, the product of the number of observations and the unadjusted R^2 from Step 3. Under the null hypothesis of homoscedasticity, LM has a χ^2 distribution with one d.f. The steps to get more efficient estimates are as follows.

1. Regress E_t against a constant and Y_t.
2. Save the residual $\hat{u}_t = E_t - \hat{\beta}_1 - \hat{\beta}_2 Y_t$.
3. Regress $\ln(\hat{u}_t^2)$ against a constant and $\ln(P_t)$ and the compute $\hat{\alpha}$ and $\hat{\beta}$ from it.
4. Estimate σ_t^2 by $\hat{\sigma}_t^2 = \hat{\alpha} P_t^{\hat{\beta}}$.

5. Compute the weight as $w_t = 1/\hat{\sigma}_t$.

6. Obtain WLS estimates by regressing $(w_t E_t)$ against w_t and $w_t Y_t$ with no constant term.

EX 8.8

a. Because the errors still satisfy the assumptions $E(u_t) = 0$ and $E(X_t u_t) = 0$, OLS estimates are unbiased and consistent. However, since the errors are heteroscedastic, estimates are inefficient.

b. Divide both sides of the equation $Y_t = \beta X_t + u_t$ by X_t so that the transformed equation is

$$\frac{Y_t}{X_t} = \beta + \frac{u_t}{X_t}$$

It is easy to verify that the variance of u_t / X_t is a constant and hence we can apply OLS to the above equation and obtain estimates that are BLUE.

c. Because the model has just a constant term, the OLS estimate is simply the mean of the transformed dependent variable. Thus, $\hat{\beta} = \frac{1}{n} \Sigma \frac{Y_t}{X_t}$. Geometrically, connect each of the observation points (X_t, Y_t) to the origin and compute its slope. The average of these slopes is the WLS estimate of β.

EX 8.9

(A) $PRICE_t = \beta_0 + \beta_1\, SQFT_t + \beta_2\, YARD_t + \beta_3\, POOL_t + u_t$

a. $\mathrm{Var}(u_t) = \sigma_t^2 = \sigma^2\, SQFT_t$, $\sigma_t = \sigma\sqrt{SQFT_t}$. Divide every term by $\sqrt{SQFT_t}$.

$$(B) \quad \frac{PRICE_t}{\sqrt{SQFT_t}} = \beta_0 \frac{1}{\sqrt{SQFT_t}} + \beta_1 \sqrt{SQFT_t} + \beta_2 \frac{YARD_t}{\sqrt{SQFT_t}} + \beta_3 \frac{POOL_t}{\sqrt{SQFT_t}} + \frac{u_t}{\sqrt{SQFT_t}}$$

Let $v_t = u_t / \sqrt{SQFT_t}$.

$$\text{Var}(v_t) = \text{Var}\left[\frac{u_t}{\sqrt{SQFT_t}}\right] = \frac{1}{SQFT_t} \cdot \sigma^2 SQFT_t = \sigma^2.$$

Therefore v_t is well behaved and OLS can be applied to Model B. This consists of regressing $PRICE/\sqrt{SQFT}$ against $1/\sqrt{SQFT}$, $\sqrt{SQFT}$, $YARD/\sqrt{SQFT}$, and $POOL/\sqrt{SQFT}$.

b. Auxiliary equation is now

$$\text{(C)} \quad \sigma_t^2 = \alpha_0 + \alpha_1 SQFT_t + \alpha_2 YARD_t + \alpha_3 POOL_t + \alpha_4 SQFT_t^2 + \alpha_5 YARD_t^2 + \alpha_6 SQFT_t * YARD_t + \alpha_7 SQFT_t * POOL_t + \alpha_8 YARD_t * POOL_t$$

First estimate (A) by OLS and save $\hat{u}_t = PRICE_t - \hat{\beta}_0 - \hat{\beta}_1 SQFT_t - \hat{\beta}_2 YARD_t - \hat{\beta}_3 POOL_t$.

Then get $\hat{u}_t^2$, $SQFT^2$, $YARD^2$, $SQFT * YARD$, $SQFT * POOL$, and $YARD * POOL$.

Estimate (C) using $\hat{u}_t^2$ for σ_t^2.

Compute $n R^2$, where n = no. of observations and R^2 is unadjusted R^2 in (C).

Null hypothesis is $H_0: \alpha_1 = \alpha_2 = \alpha_3 = \alpha_4 = \alpha_5 = \alpha_6 = \alpha_7 = \alpha_8 = 0$. Alternative is H_1: at least one of them is non-zero.

Under H_0, $n R^2 \sim \chi_8^2$.

Reject H_0 if $n R^2 > \chi_8^2(a)$, the point on χ_8^2, such that the area to the right is a, the level of significance. Alternatively, calculate $P(\chi_8^2 > n R^2)$. If this p-value $< a$ reject H_0.

EX 8.11

a. $\sigma_t^2 = \alpha_1 + \alpha_2 S_t + \alpha_3 D_t + \alpha_4 S_t^2 + \alpha_5 (S_t \times D_t)$. Note that D_t^2 is not used here because it a dummy variable.

b. $\alpha_2 = \alpha_3 = \alpha_4 = \alpha_5 = 0$.

c. Regress P_t against a constant, S_t, and D_t and obtain $\hat{u}_t = P_t - \hat{\beta}_1 - \hat{\beta}_2 S_t - \hat{\beta}_3 D_t$. Next regress $\hat{u}_t^2$ against a constant, S_t, D_t, S_t^2, and $(S_t \times D_t)$.

d. Compute LM = nR^2, where n is the number of observations and R^2 is the unadjusted R^2 from the second regression in Step c. Under the null hypothesis of homoscedasticity, LM has the χ^2 distribution with 4 d.f.

e. The critical value of χ_4^2 for a 5 percent level is 9.48773. Reject the null if LM > 9.48773.

f. From the auxiliary regression compute $\hat{\sigma}_t^2 = \hat{\alpha}_1 + \hat{\alpha}_2 S_t + \hat{\alpha}_3 D_t + \hat{\alpha}_4 S_t^2 + \hat{\alpha}_5 (S_t \times D_t)$. Next compute the weight as $w_t = 1/\sqrt{\hat{\sigma}_t^2}$. Finally, regress $w_t P_t$ against w_t, $w_t S_t$, and $w_t D_t$, without a constant term.

EX 8.12

a. $H_0: \alpha_2 = \alpha_3 = 0$. H_1: at least one of them is not zero.

b. (1) Regress E_t against a constant and Y_t, (2) compute the residuals $\hat{u}_t = E_t - \hat{\beta}_1 - \hat{\beta}_2 Y_t$, and (3) regress $\hat{u}_t^2$ against a constant, P_t, and P_t^2.

c. Compute LM = nR^2, where n = number of observations and R^2 = unadjusted R^2 from the above regression.

d. Under H_0, LM has the chi-square distribution with 2 d.f.

e. From Step (3) of Part b, estimate the error variance as $\hat{\sigma}_t^2 = \hat{\alpha}_1 + \alpha_2 P_t + \hat{\alpha}_3 P_t^2$. If $\hat{\sigma}_t^2$ is not positive for any t, then use $\hat{u}_t^2$ for that t. Compute the weight as $w_t = 1/\sqrt{\hat{\sigma}_t^2}$. Finally, regress $w_t E_t$ against w_t and $w_t Y_t$ with no constant term.

EX 8.13

a. Given $\sigma_t^2 = k\,\text{YARD}_t$. Define $w_t = 1/\sqrt{(\text{YARD}_t)}$. Next multiply each variable by w_t and generate $Y_t^* = w_t\,\text{PRICE}_t$, $X_{t1}^* = wt$, $X_{t2}^* = w_t \ln(\text{SQFT}_t)$, and $X_{t3}^* = w_t \ln(\text{YARD}_t)$. Then regress Y_t^* against X_{t1}^*, X_{t2}^*, and X_{t3}^*, with no constant term.

b. Since the weights are known, WLS estimates are BLUE and hence most efficient, that is, more efficient that OLS.

c. For the Glesjer test, one possible assumption is that $\sigma_t = \alpha_1 + \alpha_2 \text{SQFT}_t + \alpha_3 \text{YARD}_t$.

d. H_0 is $\alpha_2 = \alpha_3 = 0$.

e. First regress PRICE against a constant, ln(SQFT), and ln(YARD) and compute the residuals $\hat{u}_t = \text{PRICE}_t - \hat{\beta}_1 - \hat{\beta}_2 \ln(\text{SQFT}_t) - \hat{\beta}_3 \ln(\text{YARD}_t)$. Next estimate the auxiliary equation by regressing $|\hat{u}_t|$ against a constant, SQFT_t, and YARD_t and compute LM = nR^2, where n is the number of observations and R^2 is the unadjusted R-square in this regression. Under H_0 this has a chi-square distribution with 2 d.f.

f. Estimate σ_t by $\hat{\sigma}_t = \hat{\alpha}_1 + \hat{\alpha}_2\text{SQFT}_t + \hat{\alpha}_3\text{YARD}_t$. Compute weight $w_t = 1/\hat{\sigma}_t$. Regress $w_t\,\text{PRICE}_t$ against w_t, $w_t \ln(\text{SQFT}_t)$, and $w_t \ln(\text{YARD}_t)$ with no constant term.

EX 8.14

$S_t = \alpha + \beta A_t + u_t$, and $\sigma_t^2 = \sigma^2/N_t$. Let $w_t = 1/\sqrt{1/N_t} = \sqrt{N_t}$. Next regress $w_t S_t$ against w_t and $w_t A_t$ without a constant term.

Because we are using known weights, OLS estimates are unbiased, consistent, most efficient, and BLUE. Also all tests of hypotheses are valid.

EX 8.15

a. $\sigma_t^2 = \alpha_1 + \alpha_2 LS_t + \alpha_3 D_t + \alpha_4 LS_t^2 + \alpha_5 (LS_t \times D_t)$. Note that D_t^2 is not used here because it is a dummy variable.

b. $\alpha_2 = \alpha_3 = \alpha_4 = \alpha_5 = 0$.

c. Regress LP_t against a constant, LS_t, and D_t and obtain $\hat{u}_t = LP_t - \hat{\beta}_1 - \hat{\beta}_2 LS_t - \beta_3 D_t$. Next regress $\hat{u}_t^2$ against a constant, S_t, D_t, S_t^2, and $(S_t \times D_t)$.

d. Compute LM = $n\,R^2$, where n is the number of observations and R^2 is the unadjusted R^2 from the second regression in Step c. Under the null hypothesis of homoscedasticity, LM has the χ^2 distribution with 4 d.f.

e. Compute p-value = area in χ_4^2 to the right of LM. Reject the null if p-value is less than the level of significance. Alternatively, look up the value of $\chi_4^2(*)$, the point on the distribution to the right of which is an area equal to level of significance. Reject the null if LM > $\chi_4^2(*)$.

f. The original OLS estimates are unbiased and consistent, but inefficient. If we use the WLS procedure, we get estimates that are biased (because an estimated variance is used to construct the weights) but consistent and asymptotically (that is, for large samples) efficient.

EX 8.16

a. Differentiating PRICE partially with respect to SQFT, we get $\partial PRICE/\partial SQFT = \beta_2 + (\beta_3/SQFT)$. For this to decrease as SQFT increases, β_3 must be positive. Similarly, β_5 should be positive.

b. Given that Var(u) = kYARD where k is a constant. This means that the standard deviation $\sigma_t = \sqrt{k\text{YARD}}$. For WLS, the weight wt should be proportional to the reciprocal of the s.d. and therefore wt = $1/\sqrt{\text{YARD}}$. We create the following variables:

PRICE* = wt*PRICE, SQFT* = wt*SQFT, LNSQFT* = wt*LNSQFT, YARD* = wt*YARD, LNYARD* = wt*LNYARD.

Next regress PRICE* against wt, SQFT*, LNSQFT*, YARD*, and LNYARD*. [Note that this will not have a constant term.]

c. If the weights are known, WLS procedure gives us estimates that are BLUE and hence most efficient. Also, tests of hypotheses are valid whereas they are not if OLS were used.

d. The auxiliary equation is

$$\begin{aligned}\ln(\sigma_t^2) &= \alpha_1 + \alpha_2 \text{SQFT} + \alpha_3 \ln(\text{SQFT}) + \alpha_4 \text{YARD} + \alpha_5 \ln(\text{YARD}) \\ &\quad + \alpha_6 \text{SQFT}^2 + \alpha_7 [\ln(\text{SQFT})]^2 + \alpha_8 \text{YARD}^2 \\ &\quad + \alpha_9 [\ln(\text{YARD})]^2\end{aligned}$$

The null hypothesis of no hsk corresponds to $\alpha_i = 0$ for i = 2, 3, ... 9, which gives us 8 restrictions.

First regress PRICE against a constant, SQFT, ln(SQFT), YARD, and ln(YARD) save the residuals as ut = PRICE - $\hat{\beta}_1 - \hat{\beta}_2$ SQFT $- \hat{\beta}_3$ ln(SQFT) $- \hat{\beta}_4$ YARD $- \hat{\beta}_5$ ln(YARD). Next generate lnusq = ln(ut*ut). Then regress lnusq against a constant, SQFT, ln(SQFT), YARD, ln(YARD), SQFT squared, ln(SQFT) squared, YARD squared, and ln(YARD) squared. The test statistic is nR^2, that is, the number of observations multiplied by the unadjusted Rsquare in the above regression. It has a chi-square distribution with 8 d.f.

EX 8.17

$\sigma_t^2 = \alpha_1 + \alpha_2 pop_t + \alpha_3 pop_t^2$. The null hypothesis is $\alpha_2 = \alpha_3 = 0$. The test statistic is LM = 51 $\times$ 0.119 = 6.069. Under the null, LM ~ χ_2^2. For a 5 percent level, the critical $LM^* = 5.99146$. Because $LM > LM^*$, we reject H_0 and conclude that there is significant HSK.

Using the auxiliary regression, estimate the residual variance as $\sigma_t^2 = -1.37791 + 1.37239\ pop_t - 0.04124\ pop_t^2$. Next compute $w_t = 1/\sqrt{(\hat{\sigma}_t^2)}$. Finally, regress w_tEXPTRAV$_t$ against w_t and w_tINCOME$_t$ with no constant term.

EX 8.18

a. $\sigma_t = \alpha_1 + \alpha_2 X_t + \alpha_3 X_t^2 + \alpha_4 S_t + \alpha_4 S_t^2$. H_0 is $\alpha_2 = \alpha_3 = \alpha_4 = \alpha_5 = 0$.

b. $LM = nR^2 = 51 \times 0.417 = 21.267$. Under H_0 it has the Chi-square distribution with 4 d.f. For a 1 percent test, the critical value is $LM^* = 13.2767$. Since $LM > LM^*$, we reject homoscedasticity and conclude that there is significant heteroscedasticity.

c. OLS estimates are still unbiased and consistent but not BLUE or efficient. Also, hypothesis tests are invalid.

d. Compute $\hat{\sigma}_t = 6.619 - 0.683\ X_t + 0.017\ X_t^2 + 0.063\ S_t - 0.003 S_t^2$. Then define $w_t = 1/\hat{\sigma}_t$. Next regress $w_t Y_t$ against, w_t, $w_t X_t$, and $w_t S_t$ without a constant term.

EX 8.19

The ESL commands needed to carry out the full analysis are too numerous to list here. They are in the disk obtainable from the author. It will be seen from the results that the new model introduced here does not do well compared to the ones used in the application section 8.4 perhaps because the explanatory variables are highly multicollinear. For this reason, we do not present a detailed summary table as asked here.

EX 8.20

The following ESL commands will be helpful here.

```
ols exptrav const income ;
genr lnusq=ln(uhat*uhat)
genr lnpop=ln(pop)
(* Auxiliary regression for LM test *)
ols lnusq 0 lnpop ;
genr LM=$nrsq
```

```
pvalue 3 1 LM
(* compute sigma hat squared from this regression *)
genr sgmasq=exp(lnusq-uhat)
genr wt=1/sqrt(sgmasq)
wls wt exptrav const income ;
```

For the auxiliary regression, LM = nR^2 = 10.87548 whose p-value is less than 0.001. Hence there is strong hsk along the lines suggested in this exercise. The estimated model using FGLS is given below.

VARIABLE	COEFFICIENT	STDERROR	T STAT	2Prob(t > |T|)
constant	0.906571	0.355793	2.548029	0.01402 **
income	0.051898	0.006782	7.65278	< 0.0001 ***

Unadjusted R-squared 0.853 Adjusted R-squared 0.850

The results are similar to those in Section 8.3.

EX 8.21

To carry out the empirical analysis here use the following ESL commands.

```
ols exptrav const income ;
genr usq=uhat*uhat
genr sqpop=pop*pop
(* Auxiliary regression for LM test *)
ols usq 0 pop sqpop ;
genr usqhat1=usq-uhat
genr LM=$nrsq
(* p-value is significant only at the 10 percent level *)
pvalue 3 2 LM
(* print values and note that several are negative *)
print usqhat1 ;
(* replace negative values by original uhat squared *)
genr d=(usqhat1>0.0)
genr usqhat2=(d*usqhat1)+((1-d)*usq)
(* compute weights *)
genr wt=1/sqrt(usqhat2)
wls wt exptrav const income ;
```

For the auxiliary regression, LM = nR^2 = 4.652982 whose p-value is 0.097638. Hence hsk is somewhat less severe here compared to the previous exercise. The estimated results are similar to those in Section 8.3.

VARIABLE	COEFFICIENT	STDERROR	T STAT	2Prob(t > |T|)
constant	0.449636	0.118009	3.810194	0.000388 ***
income	0.056366	0.005796	9.725532	< 0.0001 ***

Unadjusted R-squared 0.853 Adjusted R-squared 0.850

EX 8.22

The table in Exercise 8.17 cannot be verified with DATA8-2 because the former was based on data obtained for an earlier edition of the book. Since the auxiliary equation for the error variance is the same as in Exercise 8.21, the results would be identical to that.

EX 8.23

The ESL commands for the basic analysis are the following.

```
ols price const sqft yard pool ;
genr usq=uhat*uhat
(* generate squares and cross product *)
square -o sqft yard pool ;
(* estimate the most general model for White's test *)
ols usq const sqft yard pool sq_sqft sq_yard yar_pool ;
genr LM1=$nrsq
pvalue 3 6 LM1
(* although LM fails to reject hsk, some of the auxiliary error terms
are significant. Retest with a smaller model *)
ols usq const sqft pool sq_sqft yar_pool ;
genr LM2=$nrsq
genr usqhat1=usq-uhat
pvalue 3 4 LM2
(* p-value indicates significance at less than 10 percent *)
print usqhat1 ;
(* one value is negative; replace it with uhat squared *)
genr d=(usqhat1>0.0)
```

```
genr usqhat2=(d*usqhat1)+((1-d)*usq)
genr wt=1/sqrt(usqhat2)
(* obtain WLS estimates *)
wls wt price const sqft yard pool ;
(* omit pool which is insignificant *)
omit pool ;
```

The estimated coefficients for the final model are similar to those obtained earlier.

VARIABLE	COEFFICIENT	STDERROR	T STAT	2Prob(t > |T|)
constant	-65.286475	44.823042	-1.456538	0.150828
sqft	0.119627	0.022298	5.365007	< 0.0001 ***
yard	0.005496	0.00143	3.84274	0.000313 ***

R-squared is computed as the square of the corr. between observed and predicted dep. var.

Unadjusted R-squared 0.413 Adjusted R-squared 0.392

EX 8.24

The ESL commands needed for this exercise are given below.

```
logs sqft yard ;
ols price const sqft l_sqft yard l_yard ;
(* compute ln sigma hat squared for the Harvey-Godfrey test *)
genr lnusq=ln(uhat*uhat)
ols lnusq const sqft l_sqft yard l_yard ;
genr LM=$nrsq
(* p-value indicates significant heteroscedasticity *)
pvalue 3 4 LM
(* estimate sigma hat squared and compute weight *)
genr sigmasq=exp(lnusq-uhat)
genr wt=1/sqrt(sigmasq)
wls wt price const sqft l_sqft yard l_yard ;
(* omit l_yard which is insignficant *)
omit l_yard ;
```

The final estimated model shows the expected diminishing marginal effect for the living area.

VARIABLE	COEFFICIENT	STDERROR	T STAT	2Prob(t > |T|)
constant	3355.832209	1434.263498	2.33976	0.022954 **
sqft	0.356593	0.111986	3.184262	0.00239 ***
l_sqft	-513.851354	218.66021	-2.349999	0.022389 **
yard	0.005458	5.824176e-04	9.370651	< 0.0001 ***

R-squared is computed as the square of the corr. between observed and predicted dep. var.

Unadjusted R-squared 0.482 Adjusted R-squared 0.454

CHAPTER 9

PRACTICE PROBLEMS

PP 9.1

The equation for the residuals is $u_t = \rho u_{t-1} + \varepsilon_t$. The null and alternative hypotheses are $\rho = 0$ and $\rho > 0$. The test would reject the null hypothesis if the Durbin-Watson statistic d is lower than d_L, where the latter is obtained from Appendix Table A.5. Practice Computer Session 5.1 provides the necessary statistics for this test. The following table presents the Durbin-Watson statistics, the associated bounds (for a one-sided test), and the decision rule.

Model	k'	DW d	d_L	d_U	Decision
A	2	0.846	1.17	1.54	Reject
B	2	0.832	1.17	1.54	Reject
C	3	0.831	1.08	1.66	Reject

We note that the null hypothesis of no autocorrelation is rejected for all three models. This means that OLS estimates are inefficient, although unbiased and consistent.

PP 9.2

The following ESL commands will be useful in obtaining the necessary test statistic for Model A of Example 5.1. The commands are similar for the other two models.

```
ols housing 0 intrate pop ;
(* save residuals for Model A above *)
genr ua = uhat
(* obtain u(t-1) *)
genr ua1 = ua(-1)
(* suppress the first observation for 1963 *)
smpl 1964 ;
(* auxiliary regression for Model A *)
ols ua 0 ua1 intrate pop;
(* compute nRsquare and p-value *)
```

```
genr LM = $nrsq
pvalue 3 1 LM
```

The nR^2 statistic and the corresponding p-value for the three models are in the following table.

Model	nR^2	p-value
A	7.018	0.008
B	7.261	0.007
C	7.266	0.007

The low p-values reinforce the conclusion of Practice Problem 9.1, namely, there is strong serial correlation among the residuals of the models.

PP 9.3

The following ESL commands will generate the information needed to answer this question.

```
logs 1 2 3 4 ;
ols 5 0 6 7 8 ;
corc 5 0 6 7 8 ;
hilu 5 0 6 7 8 ;
```

For that data, $n = 30$, $k' = 3$, $d = 0.981$, $d_L = 1.21$, and $d_U = 1.65$. Because $d < d_L$, there is evidence of serial correlation. The appropriate estimation procedure is either HILU or CORC. We note that these two procedures give estimates which are quite close.

EXERCISES

EX 9.2

It is given that the estimated model is based on cross-section data. In this case, serial correlation test is meaningless. This is because, cross-section data can be rearranged and so we will get different values for the DW statistic. This suggests that the DW test is nonsensical. With cross section data you never have to worry about serial correlation.

EX 9.3

We have $n = 27$, $k' = 2$, $d = 0.65$, $d_L = 1.24$, and $d_U = 1.56$. Because $d < d_L$, a significant first-order autocorrelation is indicated. By Property 9.1, estimates and forecasts are unbiased and consistent, but inefficient. Tests of hypotheses are invalid and the goodness of fit is generally exaggerated. A procedure that gives more efficient estimates is the CORC procedure; (1) regress *LH* against a constant, *LY*, and *LP*, and save $\hat{u}_t$, (2) compute $\hat{\rho}$ from equation (9.7), (3) obtain $LH_t^* = LH_t - \hat{\rho} LH_{t-1}$, $LY_t^* = LY_t - \hat{\rho}\, LY_{t-1}$, and $LP_t^* = LP_t - \hat{\rho}\, LP_{t-1}$, (4) regress LH_t^* against a constant, LY_t^*, and LP_t^* and obtain the parameter estimates and a new $\hat{u}_t$, (5) go back to step (2) and iterate until two successive $\hat{\rho}$ values do not differ much.

EX 9.5

We have, $n = 32$, $k' = 1$, $d = 0.207$, $d_L = 1.37$, and $d_U = 1.50$. Let the error term be $u_t = \rho u_{t-1} + \varepsilon_t$ where ε_t is "well-behaved." The null hypothesis is $\rho = 0$ and the alternative is $\rho > 0$. Because $d < d_L$ we reject the null hypothesis and conclude that there is significant first-order autocorrelation. We are not justified in feeling that the fit is excellent and that the coefficients are highly significant. This is because serial correlation makes the tests invalid and the goodness of fit is generally exaggerated.

EX 9.6

a. $u_t = \rho\, u_{t-1} + \varepsilon_t$. $H_0: \rho = 0$.

b. We have, $k' = 4$ and $n = 41$. d_L is in the range (1.285, 1.336). d_U is in the range (1.720, 1.721).

c. $d = 0.97 < d_L$. Therefore we reject H_0 and conclude that there is significant serial correlation.

d. OLS estimates are unbiased and consistent but not efficient (that is, not BLUE). Hypothesis tests are invalid.

e. The list of reasons include:

   1. DW test can (and often does) lead to an inconclusive test.

   2. The test is not applicable for higher order serial correlation.

3. The test is not valid if the model contains lagged dependent variables; Y_{t-1}, Y_{t-2}, etc.
4. If the number of variables is large, the DW table may not have the critical values.
5. DW test gives critical values only for a limited set of levels of significance. LM test and p-value can be used for any level. However, some programs such as SHAZAM do give p-values for the DW d and can be used.

f. First transform the model as follows.

$$\ln(Q_t) - \rho \ln(Q_{t-1}) = \beta_1(1-\rho) + \beta_2[\ln(P_t - \rho\ln(P_{t-1})] + \beta_3[\ln(Y_t - \rho\ln(Y_{t-1})] + \beta_4[\ln(ACCID_t - \rho\ln(ACCID_{t-1})] + \beta_5[\ln(FATAL_t - \rho\ln(FATAL_{t-1})] + \varepsilon_t$$

Next fix ρ, at say ρ_1, to be any value between −1 and +1. Generate the variables $Q_t^* = \ln(Q_t) - \rho_1\ln(Q_{t-1})$, $X_{t2}^* = \ln(P_t) - \rho_1\ln(P_{t-1})$, and so on to X_{t5}^*. Then regress Q_t^* against a constant, X_{t2}^*, and so on to X_{t5}^*, and compute the error sum of squares ESS. Vary ρ_1 from −1 to +1 and choose the value $\hat{\rho}$ at which ESS is minimum. Then use this final $\hat{\rho}$ and transform to obtain new Q_t^* etc. Finally, regress Q_t^*, against a constant, X_{t2}^*, and so on to X_{t5}^* to complete estimates and related statistics.

EX 9.7

a. $u_t = \rho_1 u_{t-1} + \rho_2 u_{t-2} + \rho_3 u_{t-3} + \rho_4 u_{t-4} + \varepsilon_t$.

b. H_0: $\rho_1 = \rho_2 = \rho_3 = \rho_4 = 0$.
H_1: At least on of the ρs is not zero.

c. Regress LH_t against a constant, LY_t, and Lr_t. Compute $\hat{u}_t = LH_t - \hat{\alpha} - \hat{\beta}LY_t - \hat{\gamma}Lr_t$. Then regress $\hat{u}_t$ against a constant, LY_t, Lr_t, $\hat{u}_{t-1}$, $\hat{u}_{t-2}$, $\hat{u}_{t-3}$, and $\hat{u}_{t-4}$ using observations 5 through n.

d. Compute LM = $(n-4)R^2 = 36R^2$ where R^2 is the unadjusted R-square for the third step above.

e. Under the null hypothesis, LM has the chi-square distribution with 4 d.f.

f. Compute p-value = area to the right of LM in χ_4^2. Reject H_0 if p-value < 0.10.

g. Forecasts are unbiased, consistent, but not efficient.

h.

Step 1: Regress LH_t against a constant, LY_t, and Lr_t.

Step 2: Compute $\hat{u}_t = LH_t - \hat{\alpha} - \hat{\beta}\, LY_t - \hat{\gamma}\, Lr_t$.

Step 3: Regress $\hat{u}_t$ against $\hat{u}_{t-1}$, $\hat{u}_{t-2}$, $\hat{u}_{t-3}$, and $\hat{u}_{t-4}$,using observations 5 through n, and obtain $\hat{\rho}_i$, $i = 1 \ldots 4$.

Step 4: Generate $LH_t^* = LH_t - \rho_1 LH_{t-1} - \ldots\ldots - \rho_4 LH_{t-4}$ and similarly for LY and Lr.

Step 5: Regress LH_t^* against a constant, LY_t^*, and Lr_t^* to get new $\hat{\alpha}, \hat{\beta}$, and $\hat{\gamma}$.

Step 4: Go back to Step 2 and iterate until the error sum of squares from Step 4 does not change by more than some specified percent (say one percent).

EX 9.8

a. $u_t = \rho\, u_{t-1} + \varepsilon_t$.

b. $H_0; \rho = 0, \quad H_1: \rho > 1$.

c. We have, $k' = 5$ and $n = 40$. $d_L = 1.230$ and $d_U = 1.786$. Because $d_L < d < d_U$, the test is inconclusive.

d. $u_t = \rho_1 u_{t-1} + \rho_2 u_{t-2} + \varepsilon_t$. $H_0: \rho_1 = \rho_2 = 0$.

e. $n-2 = 38$ and $R^2 = 0.687$. Hence LM = 26.106. Under the null, LM has the chi-square distribution with 2 d.f.

f. $\text{LM}^* = 13.816 < \text{LM}$. Therefore we reject H_0 and conclude that there is significant second order serial correlation.

g.

Step 1: Regress $\ln(Q_t)$ against a constant, $\ln(K_t)$, $\ln(L_t)$, $\ln(A_t)$, $\ln(F_t)$, and $\ln(S_t)$.

Step 2: Compute $\hat{u}_t = \ln(Q_t) - \hat{\beta}_1 - \hat{\beta}_2 \ln(K_t) - \ldots\ldots - \hat{\beta}_6 \ln(S_t)$.

Step 3: Regress $\hat{u}_t$ against $\hat{u}_{t-1}$ and $\hat{u}_{t-2}$ with no constant.

Step 4: Generate $Y_t^* = \ln(Q_t) - \hat{\rho}_1 \ln(Q_{t-1}) - \hat{\rho}_2 \ln(Q_{t-2})$. $X_{t2}^* = \ln(K_t) - \hat{\rho}_1 \ln(K_{t-1}) - \hat{\rho}_2 \ln(K_{t-2})$, and similarly for the other explanatory variables.

Step 5: Regress Y_t^* against a constant and the X^* variables and obtain new estimates of the βs.

Step 6: Go back to Step 2 and iterate until the error sum of squares for Step 4 does not change by more than a certain percentage, say, 0.01 percent.

EX 9.9

a. $u_t = \rho_1 u_{t-1} + \rho_2 u_{t-2} + \rho_3 u_{t-3} + \varepsilon_t$.

b. H_0: $\rho_1 = \rho_2 = \rho_3 = 0$.

c. $\text{LM} = (n-3)R^2 = 6.291$.

d. Under H_0, LM has the chi-square distribution with 3 d.f.

e. For a 10 percent test, the critical $\text{LM}^* = 6.25139$.

f. Since $\text{LM} > \text{LM}^*$, we reject the null and hence conclude that there is significant serial correlation.

g. Since serial correlation exists, OLS estimators are unbiased and consistent, but not BLUE (that is, not efficient), and all tests are invalid.

EX 9.10

a. $SR_t = RFR_t + \alpha MR_t - \alpha RFR_t + v_t = RFR_t(1-\alpha) + \alpha MR_t + v_t$. Therefore, $\beta_1 = 0, \beta_2 = \alpha$, and $\beta_3 = 1-\alpha$. The relevant restrictions are $\beta_1 = 0$ and $\beta_2 + \beta_3 = 1$.

b. First regress SR_t against a constant, MR_t, and RFR_t, and save the error sum of squares as *ESSA*. Next generate $Y_t = SR_t - RFR_t$ and $X_t = MR_t - RFR_t$. Then regress Y_t against X_t without a constant term and save the error sum of squares as *ESSB*.

c. Compute $F_c = \dfrac{(ESSB - ESSA)/2}{ESSA/(n-3)}$.

d. Under the null hypothesis, F_c has the F-distribution with 2 d.f. for the numerator and $n-3$ d.f. for the denominator.

e. The transformed model is:

$$(C)\quad SR_t - \rho\, SR_{t-1} = \beta_1(1-\rho) + \beta_2(MR_t - \rho\, MR_{t-1}) + \beta_3(RFR_t - \rho\, RFR_{t-1}) + \varepsilon_t$$

Step 1: Choose ρ at a fixed value. Then generate $SR_t^* = SR_t - \rho\, SR_{t-1}$, $MR_t^* = MR_t - \rho\, MR_{t-1}$, and $RFR_t^* = RFR_t - \rho\, RFR_{t-1}$.

Step 2: Regress SR_t^* against a constant, MR_t^*, and RFR_t^*, and get ESSC.

Step 3: Vary ρ at broad steps from -0.99 through + 0.99 say at steps of length 0.1. Choose the $\hat{\rho}$ that minimizes ESSC as the starting point of a CORC iteration.

Step 4: Repeat Step 2 after using this $\hat{\rho}$ in Step 1 and compute $\hat{u}_t = SR_t - \hat{\beta}_1 - \hat{\beta}_2 MR_t - \hat{\beta}_3 RFR_t$.

Step 5: Get new estimate $\hat{\rho} = [\sum(\hat{u}_t\, \hat{u}_{t-1})]/[\sum \hat{u}_{t-1}^2]$.

Step 6: Repeat Steps 1, 2, 4, and 5, using new $\hat{\rho}$ values and iterate until $\hat{\rho}$ from two successive iterations do not change more than say 0.001.

Step 7: Using this final $\hat{\rho}$ estimate Model C.

EX 9.11

$$LQ_t = \beta_1 + \beta_2 LP_t + \beta_3 LY_t + u_t.$$

a. $u_t = \rho_1 u_{t-1} + \rho_2 u_{t-2} + \rho_3 u_{t-3} + \rho_4 u_{t-4} + \varepsilon_t.$
$H_0: \rho_1 = \rho_2 = \rho_3 = \rho_4 = 0.$

b.

1. Regress LQ against 0, LP, and LY, and get $\hat{u}_t = LQ_t - \hat{\beta}_1 - \hat{\beta}_2 LP_t - \hat{\beta}_3 LY_t$.
2. Generate $\hat{u}_{t-1}$, $\hat{u}_{t-2}$, $\hat{u}_{t-3}$, and $\hat{u}_{t-4}$.
3. Regress $\hat{u}_t$ against $\hat{u}_{t-1}$, $\hat{u}_{t-2}$, $\hat{u}_{t-3}$, $\hat{u}_{t-4}$, constant, LP_t, and LY_t, *using only observations 5 through n.*
4. Compute $(n-4)R^2$ where n = *no.* of observations and R^2 is unadjusted R^2 from (b.3). Under H_o, $(n-4)R^2 \sim \chi_4^2$.
5. Reject H_o if $P[\chi_4^2 > (n-4)R^2] <$ level of significance or if $(n-4)R^2 > \chi_4^2(*)$, the point on χ_4^2 such that the area to the right is equal to the level of significance.

c.

1. Regress LQ against 0, LP_t, and LY_t.
2. Get $\hat{u}_t = LQ_t - \hat{\beta}_1 - \hat{\beta}_2 \, LP_t - \hat{\beta}_3 \, LY_t$.
3. Generate $\hat{u}_{t-1}$, $\hat{u}_{t-2}$, $\hat{u}_{t-3}$, and $\hat{u}_{t-4}$.
4. Regress $\hat{u}_t$ against $\hat{u}_{t-1}$, $\hat{u}_{t-2}$, $\hat{u}_{t-3}$, and $\hat{u}_{t-4}$ [Note: no constant term here and no LP_t or LY_t] and get $\hat{\rho}_1, \hat{\rho}_2, \hat{\rho}_3, \hat{\rho}_4$.
5. Generate
   $LQ_t^* = LQ_t - \hat{\rho}_1 \, LQ_{t-1} - \cdots - \hat{\rho}_4 \, LQ_{t-4}$
   $LP_t^* = LP_t - \hat{\rho}_1 \, LP_{t-1} \cdots \hat{\rho}_4 \, LQ_{t-4}$
   $LY_t^* = LY_t - \hat{\rho}_1 \, LY_{t-1} \cdots - \hat{\rho}_t \, LY_{t-4}$
6. Regress LQ_t^* against 0, LP_t^*, and LY_t^* and get the next round of estimates $\hat{\beta}_1, \hat{\beta}_2$, and $\hat{\beta}_3$.
7. Go back to Step (2) and iterate until ESS for Step (6) doesn't change by more than some pre-specified number of percentage.

d. Estimates are biased, but consistent, and *asymptotically* efficient.

EX 9.12

a. As money supply increases, interest rates will fall. This stimulates investment and increases Y_t.

   As government expenditure increases, aggregate demand increases which will expand Y_t.

   As taxes increase, disposable income decreases, consumption demand will decline and Y_t will decrease.

   Increasing exports mean more jobs domestically and more production, increasing Y_t.

b. The signs for G_t and T_t are opposite of what we would expect. As the correlation matrix shows, this is due to high multicollinearity.

c. In Table A.5, $n = 104$, $k' = 4$, d_L is approximately 1.592 and d_U is approximately 1.758. Durbin-Watson $d = 0.401 < d_L$. Therefore $H_0\colon \rho = 0$ for AR(1) is rejected. This means that there is significant first-order autocorrelation. OLS estimates are still unbiased and consistent, but they are no longer efficient. Estimated variance are biased and hypothesis tests are invalid. Also, the observed R^2 will be an overestimate of the true goodness of fit.

d. $u_t = \rho_1 u_{t-1} + \rho_2 u_{t-2} + \rho_3 u_{t-3} + \rho_4 u_{t-4} + \varepsilon_t$.

H_0: $\rho_1 = \rho_2 = \rho_3 = \rho_4 = 0$.

LM = nR^2 = 68.3. Under the null this is distributed as χ^2_4. The critical value is for a 1 percent test is LM^* = 13.2767 < LM. Therefore we reject H_0 and conclude that there is significant fourth-order serial correlation.

e.

1. Regress Y against a constant, M_t, G_t, T_t, and X_t.
2. Get $\hat{u}_t = Y_t - \hat{\beta}_1 - \hat{\beta}_2 M_t - \hat{\beta}_3 G_t - \hat{\beta}_4 T_t - \hat{\beta}_5 X_t$.
3. Generate $\hat{u}_{t-1}$, $\hat{u}_{t-2}$, $\hat{u}_{t-3}$, and $\hat{u}_{t-4}$.
4. Regress $\hat{u}_t$ against $\hat{u}_{t-1}$, $\hat{u}_{t-2}$, $\hat{u}_{t-3}$, and $\hat{u}_{t-4}$ (with no constant term) and get $\hat{\rho}_1, \hat{\rho}_2, \hat{\rho}_3, \hat{\rho}_4$.
5. Generate
   $Y_t^* = Y_t - \hat{\rho}_1 Y_{t-1} - \cdots - \hat{\rho}_4 Y_{t-4}$
   $M_t^* = M_t - \hat{\rho}_1 M_{t-1} \cdots \hat{\rho}_4 M_{t-4}$
   and similarly for the other variables.
6. Regress Y_t^* against a constant, M_t^*, G_t^*, T_t^*, and X_t^*, and get the next round of estimates for the βs.
7. Go back to Step (2) and iterate until ESS for Step (6) does not change by more than some pre-specified number of percentage.

EX 9.13

To obtain the empirical results for this exercise, use the following ESL commands.

```
genr lph = ln(housing/pop)
genr lpcgnp = ln(gnp/pop)
genr lr = ln(intrate)
(* estimate model by OLS procedure *)
ols lph 0 lpcgnp lr ;
(* LM test for AR(1) *)
genr ut = uhat
genr ut1 = ut(-1)
smpl 1964 ;
ols ut 0 ut1 lpcgnp lr ;
```

```
genr LM1 = $nrsq
pvalue 3 1 LM1
(* reset sample range to the beginning and estimate by hilu-corc *)
smpl 1963 ;
hilu lph 0 lpcgnp lr;
(* LM test for AR(3) *)
genr ut2 = ut(-2)
genr ut3 = ut(-3)
smpl 1966 ;
ols ut 0 ut1 ut2 ut3 lpcgnp lr ;
genr LM3 = $nrsq
pvalue 3 3 LM3
smpl 1963 ;
(* estimate model by AR procedure *)
ar 1 2 3 ; lph 0 lpcgnp lr ;
ar 1 2 ; lph 0 lpcgnp lr ;
```

We have, n = 23, k' = 2, Durbin-Watson statistic d = 0.808, and d_L = 1.17. Because $d < d_L$, we conclude that there is significant first-order serial correlation. For the LM test, nR^2 = 7.617 and the corresponding p-value is 0.0058, which is extremely low. The LM test thus confirms the DW-test. Because serial correlation is present, OLS estimates are inefficient although unbiased and consistent.

When the model was estimated by the mixed HILU-CORC procedure, DW d was 1.002 which suggests that autocorrelation persists. An LM test for AR(3) was next performed. nR^2 for this is 14.295 with a p-value 0.0025 which is considerably small suggesting support for the hypothesis that the residuals follow an AR(3) process. The model was then reestimated by the AR procedure and it was found that the AR(3) term is very insignificant. AR(2) was next applied and the estimated values and associated statistics are given in the next page.

The model explains 90.9 percent of the variation in the logarithm of per capita housing starts and all the coefficients are significant at levels below 0.01 percent. As expected, the interest rate elasticity is negative. The income elasticity is extremely high indicating that a one percent increase in per capita income is expected to increase per capita housing demand by 3.7 percent. Demand is also elastic with respect to the interest rate but the numerical value is much lower.

VARIABLE	COEFFICIENT	STDERROR	T STAT	PROB t > |T|
constant	-3.53350	1.14462	-3.087	0.0064 ***
lpcgnp	3.69482	0.61184	6.039	< 0.0001 ***
lr	-1.76622	0.23275	-7.588	< 0.0001 ***
ESTIMATES OF THE AR COEFFICIENTS				
ut_1	1.20872	0.13601	8.887	< 0.0001 ***
ut_2	-0.77819	0.12403	-6.274	< 0.0001 ***

Adjusted R-squared (computed as the square of the corr. between observed and predicted dep. var.) is 0.909.

The model might suffer from the "omitted variable bias", however, because there is no price index of housing included in the model.

EX 9.14

The following ESL commands will be useful in obtaining the output needed to answer the questions here.

```
ols profits 0 sales;
(* LM test for first-order serial correlation *)
genr ut=uhat
genr time
graph ut time;
genr ut1 = ut(-1)
smpl 1975 ;
ols ut 0 sales ut1;
genr LM1 = $nrsq
pvalue 3 1 LM1
smpl 1974 ;
corc profits 0 sales;
hilu profits 0 sales;
(* LM test for higher order serial correlation *)
genr ut2 = ut(-2)
genr ut3 = ut(-3)
smpl 1977 ;
ols ut 0 ut1 ut2 ut3 sales ;
genr LM3 = $nrsq
pvalue 3 3 LM3
```

```
smpl 1974 ;
ar 1 2 3 ; profits 0 sales ;
ar 1 2 ; profits 0 sales ;
```

The residual plot exhibits a clustering effect indicating serial correlation. $n = 21$, $k' = 1$, $d = 1.08$, and $d_L = 1.221$. There is evidence of serial correlation ($d < d_L$) here. For the LM test, regress $\hat{u}_t$ against a constant, sales, and $\hat{u}_{t-1}$. For this auxiliary regression $nR^2 = 3.541$ with a p-value of 0.0599 which is significant at the 6 percent level. The estimates using CORC and the mixed HILU-CORC are quite close. The DW statistic for the residuals of the transformed model is 1.2, which is significant. A test for higher order serial correlation is therefore indicated. nR^2 for AR(3) is 12.598 with a p-value of 0.0056, which makes AR(3) significant. The model was then reestimated by the AR procedure and it was found that the AR(3) term is very insignificant. AR(2) was next applied and the estimated values and associated statistics are given below.

```
------------------------------------------------------------------------
VARIABLE        COEFFICIENT        STDERROR        T STAT    2Prob(t > |T|)

constant          38.567037       18.142254      2.125813      0.048471 **
sales              0.025547        0.008043      3.176263      0.005522 ***

ESTIMATES OF THE AR COEFFICIENTS

ut_1               0.986529        0.190825       5.16982      < 0.0001 ***
ut_2              -0.955998        0.196936     -4.854358      0.000149 ***

R-squared is computed as the square of the corr. between observed and
predicted dep. var.

Unadjusted R-squared      0.702      Adjusted R-squared                0.685
------------------------------------------------------------------------
```

Both the AR terms are significant at the 5 percent level and the sales coefficient is significant at the 1 percent level. The model explains only 68.5 percent of the variation in profits. A one thousand dollar increase in sales is expected to increase the profits, on average, by $25.55.

EX 9.15

The following ESL commands will be helpful in estimating this model.

```
logs demand income price temp;
ols l_demand 0 l_income l_price l_temp;
genr ut=uhat
```

```
lags ut;
print ut ut_1;
corc l_demand 0 l_income l_price l_temp;
hilu l_demand 0 l_income l_price l_temp;
smpl 2;
ols ut 0 l_income l_price l_temp ut_1;
genr LM = $nrsq
pvalue 3 1 LM
```

a. The error term is assumed to be $u_t = \rho u_{t-1} + \varepsilon_t$, the null hypothesis is $\rho = 0$, and the alternative is $\rho > 0$. For the DW test, $d = 0.981$, $n = 30$, $k' = 3$, $d_L = 1.21$, and $d_U = 1.65$. There is evidence of first-order autocorrelation because $d < d_L$. For the LM test, estimate the model and obtain $\hat{u}_t$. Then regress $\hat{u}_t$ against a constant, l_price, l_income, l_temp, and $\hat{u}_{t-1}$. $(n-1)R^2 = 6.098$. Because the corresponding p-value is 0.014, we reject the null hypothesis (at 1.4 percent) and conclude that there is significant autocorrelation.

b. By Property 9.1, estimates are unbiased and consistent but inefficient.

c. *HILU procedure*: First generate $l\_demand_t^* = l\_demand_t - \hat{\rho}\ l\_demand_{t-1}$ (where $\hat{\rho}$ is any value between -1 and +1) and similarly for the other variables. Use these transformed variables and estimate the modified model and compute its error sum of squares (ESS). Next choose a different $\hat{\rho}$ and repeat the procedure. By systematically searching from -1 to +1, we get a series of ESS values. Choose that $\hat{\rho}$ for which ESS is the lowest. The estimates corresponding to these are the HILU estimates. Estimates are "better" in the sense of greater asymptotic efficiency.

EX 9.16

Since the book went to press, DATA9-7 has been updated and hence the model here is different from the one in Exercise 9.16. The basic model used here is

$$\ln(QNC/POP) = \alpha + \beta \ln(PRICE) + \gamma \ln(INCOME)$$
$$\delta \ln(PRIME) + \varepsilon \ln(UNEMP) + u$$

a. The ESL commands useful in obtaining the information needed to answer this question are too numerous to list here and are available in a diskette obtained from the author.

b. The correlation matrix indicates that several variables are almost perfectly collinear. Because of this, the most general model with all the dummy shifts and interactions could not be incorporated.

c. For the auxiliary regression for AR(1), $(n-1)R^2 = 29.985$ and its p-value is less than 1 percent which indicates strong first-order serial correlation. The estimates are therefore unbiased, consistent, but not BLUE. Standard errors are also inconsistent and tests of hypotheses are invalid.

d. The modification is not done here because the test for AR(4) carried out below indicates strong fourth-order autocorrelation.

e. Estimate the auxiliary regression with $\hat{u}_t$ as the dependent variable and the added independent variables, $\hat{u}_{t-1}$, $\hat{u}_{t-2}$, $\hat{u}_{t-3}$, and $\hat{u}_{t-4}$. Here $(n-4)R^2 = 33.404$ with p-value < 0.0001. Autocorrelation of order 4 is therefore suggested with the residual equation $u_t = \rho_1 u_{t-1} + \rho_2 u_{t-2} + \rho_3 u_{t-3} + \rho_4 u_{t-4} + \varepsilon_t$. The appropriate estimation procedure is the generalized CORC method described in Section 9.5. The estimated final model is given below.

VARIABLE	COEFFICIENT	STDERROR	T STAT	2Prob(t > |T|)	
constant	6.512324	1.870166	3.482217	0.001029	***
SUMMER	-1.048114	0.332664	-3.150667	0.002725	***
l_PRICE	-2.318732	0.412582	-5.620058	< 0.0001	***
SUPRICE	0.296075	0.073984	4.001878	0.000204	***
l_INCOME	2.773361	0.563104	4.925128	< 0.0001	***
SPINCOME	0.221409	0.045769	4.837579	< 0.0001	***
SPPRIME	-0.177155	0.045712	-3.875436	0.000305	***
SUPRIME	-0.119684	0.053294	-2.245751	0.029081	**
FPRIME	-0.113965	0.041915	-2.718939	0.008929	***
FUNEMP	0.123744	0.050838	2.434081	0.018471	**
ESTIMATES OF THE AR COEFFICIENTS					
ut_1	0.261726	0.122255	2.140824	0.036503	**
ut_2	0.343199	0.114009	3.010292	0.00386	***
ut_3	0.262536	0.113248	2.318241	0.023983	**

R-squared is computed as the square of the corr. between observed and predicted dep. var.

Unadjusted R-squared 0.850 Adjusted R-squared 0.823

The price elasticity in winter, the control period, is –2.319 and that in the summer is –2.023. These are considerably higher than 1 in absolute value and hence demand for cars is very price elastic. Income elasticity is also high with the values 2.773 for winter and 3.336 for spring. The prime rate has the expected negative sign in spring, summer, and fall, but is inelastic. Unemp was significant only for fall but had a positive sign which is counter-intuitive.

EX 9.17

The ESL commands that will be useful to obtain the results for this are given below.

```
logs HARVEST EXPORTS HOUSTART INDPROD
   TIMBPRIC PRODPRIC ;
ols l_HARVES const l_EXPORT l_HOUSTA l_INDPRO
  l_TIMBPR l_PRODPR ;
genr ut = uhat
genr ut1 = ut(-1)
genr ut2 = ut(-2)
genr ut3 = ut(-3)
smpl 1962 ;
ols ut const l_EXPORT l_HOUSTA l_INDPRO l_TIMBPR
  l_PRODPR ut1 ut2 ut3 ;
genr LM = $nrsq
pvalue 3 3 LM
smpl 1959 ;
ar 1 2 3 ; l_HARVES const l_EXPORT l_HOUSTA l_INDPRO
  l_TIMBPR l_PRODPR ;
ar 1 3 ; l_HARVES const l_EXPORT l_HOUSTA l_INDPRO
  l_TIMBPR l_PRODPR ;
omit l_EXPORT ;
omit l_TIMBPR ;
```

The Durbin-Watson statistics for the general model with all the explanatory variables is 0.823. From Table A.5, for n = 31 and k' = 5, we have d_L = 1.09 and d_U = 1.825. It is clear that there is significant first-order serial correlation. For the LM test, the test statistic is 11.679 with a p-value of 0.000632. Thus the LM test also supports AR(1). For the LM test for AR(3), the test statistic is 13.879 with a

p-value of 0.003075, indicating that AR(3) is significant. The generalized Cochrane-Orcutt procedure indicates that the AR(2) term is insignificant. Therefore AR(3) was reestimated after setting ρ_2 to zero. In this model, the variables l_EXPORT and l_TIMBPR were omitted because of insignificance. The final model coefficients and associated statistics, using the generalized CORC, are given below.

```
-----------------------------------------------------------------------
VARIABLE        COEFFICIENT         STDERROR       T STAT      PROB t > |T|

constant            1.29111         0.166504     7.754206     < 0.0001 ***
l_HOUSTA           0.219867         0.068953     3.188666     0.003947 ***
l_INDPRO           0.476611          0.13422      3.55097     0.001624 ***
l_PRODPR          -0.252823         0.082868    -3.050895     0.005497 ***

ESTIMATES OF THE AR COEFFICIENTS

    ut_1           0.694064         0.143273     4.844352     < 0.0001 ***
    ut_3          -0.269623         0.115527     -2.33385     0.027605 **

R-squared is computed as the square of the corr. between observed and
predicted dep. var.

Unadjusted R-squared      0.835     Adjusted R-squared             0.814
-----------------------------------------------------------------------
```

To test for unitary elasticity, the t-statistics are as follows.

$$
\begin{array}{lll}
\text{l\_HOUSTA} & t_c = (1 - 0.219867)/0.068953 & = 11.31 \\
\text{l\_INDPRO} & t_c = (1 - 0.476611)/0.13422 & = 3.90 \\
\text{l\_PRODPR} & t_c = (1 - 0.252823)/0.082868 & = 9.01
\end{array}
$$

It is easy to verify that all these are significant and therefore we conclude that elasticities are not unitary. Because they are all numerically less than 1, the coefficients are inelastic.

EX 9.18

The relevant data file for this is DATA9-8. The text file *ex9-18.esl* included in the disk has the needed ESL commands. Execute the program with the DOS command

```
ESL -v50 data9-8 -b < ex9-18.esl > ex9-18.out
```

Thc flag *-v50* is needed to override the default limit set for the number of variables. [The execution might take a while].

The Durbin-Watson $d = 0.796$, $n = 41$, $k' = 5$, $d_L = 1.23$, and $D_U = 1.79$. Because $d < d_L$, we reject the null hypothesis of no serial correlation and conclude that it is significant. This means that OLS estimates, though unbiased and consistent, are inefficient. For the LM test, $nR^2 = 19.18$ with a p-value of less than 0.0001 which is extremely low. This test also rejects the null hypothesis. CORC and HILU procedures yield estimates which are very close to each other.

To test for structural change, first create the three new variables *rl_price*, *rl_pcgnp*, and *rl_accpm* which are defined as the products of the regulation dummy variable and corresponding independent variable. The model with complete interactions is given below.

$$l\_y = \alpha_0 + \alpha_1 regu + l\_price\,(\beta_0 + \beta_1 regu) + l\_pcgnp\,(\gamma_0 + \gamma_1 regu)$$
$$+ l\_accpm\,(\delta_0 + \delta_1 regu) + \varepsilon fatal + u_t$$

This model was tested for AR(3) which was found to be present. The Generalized CORC procedure was next estimated and insignificant terms omitted one at a time until a "final" model was obtained in which all regression coefficients were significant at the 10 percent level or at a lower level. The estimated final model is given below.

```
--------------------------------------------------------------------------
VARIABLE          COEFFICIENT          STDERROR        T STAT      PROB t > |T|

constant              0.34977           0.41229         0.848        0.4022
l_price              -0.61868           0.08782        -7.045      < 0.0001 ***
rl_price              0.01689           0.00775         2.180        0.0363 **
l_pcgnp               0.97276           0.11759         8.273      < 0.0001 ***

ESTIMATES OF THE AR COEFFICIENTS

ut_1                  0.95427           0.14911         6.400      < 0.0001 ***
ut_2                  0.36794           0.18548         1.984        0.0552 *
ut_3                 -0.37427           0.12261        -3.053        0.0043 ***

Adjusted R-squared computed as the square of the corr. between observed
and predicted dep. var. is 0.999.
--------------------------------------------------------------------------
```

The model explains 99.9 percent of the variation in the logarithm of per capita revenue passenger miles and all the AR coefficients are significant. However, the regulation and fatality variables are generally not significant. The only exception is the elasticity with respect to price. When regulation was in effect (regu = 0), the price elasticity was -0.619, whereas when it was lifted the elasticity decreased (in numerical terms) to -0.602. Thus, deregulation made price slightly less elastic.

EX 9.19

Use the following ESL commands to generate the output needed to answer this question.

```
logs 2 3 4 5 6 7 8 9 ;
ols 10 0 11 12 13 14 15 16 17 ;
(* save residuals, lag them, and do LM tests for AR 1 and 3 *)
genr ut = uhat
genr ut1 = ut(-1)
genr ut2 = ut(-2)
genr ut3 = ut(-3)
smpl 1949 ;
ols ut 0 ut1 11 12 13 14 15 16 17 ;
genr LM1 = $nrsq
pvalue 3 1 LM1
smpl 1951 ;
ols ut 0 ut1 ut2 ut3 11 12 13 14 15 16 17 ;
genr LM3 = $nrsq
pvalue 3 3 LM3
(* reset sample range to the beginning and use CORC and HILU
procedures *)
smpl 1948 ;
corc 10 0 11 12 13 14 15 16 17 ;
hilu 10 0 11 12 13 14 15 16 17 ;
omit 16 ;
omit 15 ;
omit 17 ;
```

nR^2 for first-order autocorrelation is 4.636 with a p-value of 0.031. For the third-order, the test statistic is 4.704 with a p-value of 0.195. Thus AR(3) is not present, but AR(1) is. Hence we applied the CORC and HILU methods which gave very similar results. The final mixed HILU-CORC estimates after eliminating variables with insignificant coefficients are given below.

VARIABLE	COEFFICIENT	STDERROR	T STAT	2Prob(t > |T|)
constant	2.745475	1.347284	2.037784	0.048223 **
l_labor	-0.720533	0.043501	-16.563709	< 0.0001 ***
l_land	1.20644	0.366579	3.291081	0.00209 ***
l_machin	-0.328531	0.102494	-3.205368	0.002651 ***
l_energy	0.228848	0.114915	1.991457	0.05329 *

Adjusted R-squared is computed as the square of the corr. between observed and predicted dependent variable is 0.976.

The model explains 97.6 percent of the logarithm of the agricultural output index. However, several coefficients have negative elasticities which are counterintuitive. A possible explanation is multicollinearity among the explanatory variables. Although pair-wise correlations are not very high, it is possible that several independent variables are jointly collinear.

EX 9.20

Use the disk file called *ex9-20.esl* to obtain the empirical results reported here. As in Section 7.9, the estimation was done using data for the first period, namely, 1983.01 through 1986.06, but using a general specification for the error structure. nR^2 statistic for 12-th order autocorrelation is 27.523 with a p-value of 0.0065 which suggests the strong presence of serial correlation. The model was therefore estimated by the Generalized CORC procedure with an AR(12) residual equation. It was found that lags 4 and 6 were insignificant as were the dummy variables for February and March. These were then eliminated and the model estimated by the AR procedure. The final model was used to predict the loss in sales and revenues over the subsequent periods. The table on the next page summarizes the loss in sales and revenues using both the OLS procedure applied in Chapter 7 and the AR procedure applied here.

The sales loss is considerably higher when the AR estimates are used but the revenue loss is slightly less. Since the AR specification is econometrically better justified, the estimates one should go by are the ones presented here.

EX 9.21

The disk file *ex9-21.esl* has the necessary ESL commands. The output for this exercise can be obtained with the DOS command

```
ESL data9-9 -b < ex9-21.esl > ex9-21.out
```

Period	Sales loss		Revenue loss	
	OLS	AR	OLS	AR
1986.07 - 1988.10	54,209	62,730	481,575	501,511
1988.11 - 1990.05	38,467	36,166	335,597	312,813
Total	92,676	98,896	817,172	814,324

The model was first estimated by OLS and tests were performed for first-order serial correlation. nR^2 for the LM test was 6.027 with a p-value of 0.014. The CORC and HILU procedures gave extremely close results, but the unemployment coefficient was very insignificant and was omitted from further analysis. The model including seasonal dummies also had serial correlation. LM test for AR(4) gave $(n-4)R^2 = 17.708$ and the p-value 0.0014, indicating strong significance. The AR procedure was next used, insignificant residual terms were eliminated, and the model reestimated. The final model estimates are presented in the following table.

VARIABLE	COEFFICIENT	STDERROR	T STAT	2Prob(t > |T|)
constant	6.474046	2.725326	2.375512	0.021246 **
dummy_2	0.131146	0.028267	4.639595	< 0.0001 ***
l_price	-2.795903	0.631186	-4.4296	< 0.0001 ***
l_Y	3.608243	0.686743	5.254142	< 0.0001 ***
ESTIMATES OF THE AR COEFFICIENTS				
ut_2	0.320823	0.127851	2.509347	0.015187 **
ut_3	0.246071	0.118197	2.081869	0.042199 **
ut_4	0.250027	0.122608	2.039241	0.046426 **

R-squared is computed as the square of the corr. between observed and predicted dep. var.

Unadjusted R-squared 0.774 Adjusted R-squared 0.761

The model explains 76.1 percent of the variation in the logarithm of per capita car sales. All the coefficients are significant. The coefficients have the expected signs, the price elasticity is -2.8, but the income elasticity is higher (3.608). Interestingly, the interest rate effect was insignificant.

EX 9.22

The ESL commands for this exercise are given below.

```
logs Q Y P ED1 ED2 ;
(* Generate interaction terms *)
genr D82l_Y = D82*l_Y
genr D86l_Y = D86*l_Y
genr D82l_P = D82*l_P
genr D86l_P = D86*l_P
genr D82l_ED1 = D82*l_ED1
genr D86l_ED1 = D86*l_ED1
genr D82l_ED2 = D82*l_ED2
genr D86l_ED2 = D86*l_ED2
(* Estimate most general model *)
ols l_Q const l_Y l_P l_ED1 l_ED2 D82 D86 D82l_Y D82l_P
   D86l_P D82l_ED1 D82l_ED2 ;
(* Save the residuals *)
genr ut = uhat
(* Generate lag terms *)
genr ut1=ut(-1)
genr ut2=ut(-2)
genr ut3=ut(-3)
(* Reset sample and estimate auxiliary regression for AR(1) *)
smpl 1961 ;
ols ut const ut1 l_Y l_P l_ED1 l_ED2 D82 D86 D82l_Y D82l_P D86l_P
 D82l_ED1 D82l_ED2 ;
(* Compute LM test statistic and its p-value *)
genr LM1 = $nrsq
pvalue 3 1 LM1
(* Repeat steps for AR(3) *)
smpl 1963 ;
ols ut const ut1 ut2 ut3 l_Y l_P l_ED1 l_ED2 D82 D86 D82l_Y D82l_P
 D86l_P D82l_ED1 D82l_ED2 ;
genr LM2 = $nrsq
pvalue 3 3 LM2
(* Reset sample range to beginning and use Generalized CORC *)
smpl 1963 ;
```

```
ar 1 2 3 ;
l_Q const l_Y l_P l_ED1 l_ED2 D82 D86 D82l_Y D82l_P D86l_P
 D82l_ED1 D82l_ED2 ;
(* Omit variables one or two at a time *)
omit D82l_ED1 ;
omit D86 ;
omit D82l_Y ;
omit D86l_P ;
omit l_ED2 ;
omit l_ED1 -o ;
```

For the general model, the Durbin-Watson statistics for AR(1) is 2.214549. From Table A.5, for n = 29 and k' = 11, d_L = 0.612 and d_U = 2.515. Because the observed d is between the limits, the DW test is inconclusive. The LM test is, however, conclusive. The LM test statistic is 0.855313 and the corresponding p-value is 0.355054. It is clear that AR(1) is not significant even at the 35 percent level. AR(3), however, is significant because the LM test statistic is 10.196889 with a p-value of 0.016965. The generalized CORC is thus the appropriate estimation procedure. [This means that the results discussed in Exercise 7.20 which were based on OLS estimates are flawed.] The general model was estimated by this procedure and variables omitted until all coefficients were significant. The estimated final model is presented below.

```
VARIABLE          COEFFICIENT          STDERROR        T STAT       PROB t > |T|

constant            -5.322437          0.254795   -20.889082       < 0.0001 ***
l_Y                  0.773936          0.036153    21.407478       < 0.0001 ***
l_P                 -0.411129          0.073962    -5.558668       < 0.0001 ***
D82                 -1.878172            0.2033     -9.23844       < 0.0001 ***
D821_P               0.408331          0.096074     4.250171        0.00054 ***
D821_ED2            -0.532253          0.052289   -10.179065       < 0.0001 ***

COVARIANCE MATRIX OF REGRESSION COEFFICIENTS

10) l_Y          11) l_P          7) D82      16) D821_P   20) D821_ED2

0.001307        -0.002485        -0.002796       0.002314  -3.805994e-04    (10
                  0.00547         0.006512      -0.005292   9.488306e-04    (11
                                  0.041331      -0.017139       0.010268    (7
                                                  0.00923      -0.003651    (16
                                                                0.002734    (20
```

```
 0) const

-0.024779    (10
 0.045797    (11
    0.051    (7
-0.042315    (16
 0.006856    (20
 0.472155    (0

ESTIMATES OF THE AR COEFFICIENTS

ut_1                -0.594879      0.179585    -3.312513     0.003475 ***
ut_2                -0.544057      0.180665    -3.011414     0.006896 ***
ut_3                -0.557879      0.183528     -3.03975     0.006469 ***
```

The test statistics for the elasticities are given below.

Income elasticity $t_c = \dfrac{1 - 0.773936}{0.036153} = 6.253$

1960-81 Price elasticity $t_c = \dfrac{1 - 0.411129}{0.073962} = 7.962$

1982-88 Price elasticity $t_c = \dfrac{1 - 0.411129 + 0.408331}{0.00547 + 0.00923 - 0.005292} = 105.995$

Without even looking at a t-table, we can see that all these t-statistics are highly significant. Thus we reject the null hypothesis of unitary elasticities for both price and income.

EX 9.23

The following ESL commands will be useful in obtaining the results for answer this question.

```
logs Y X1 X10 X12 X13 X14 X15 ;
ols l_Y const l_X1 X3 X4 X5 X6 X7 X8 X9 l_X10
   X11 l_X12 l_X13 l_X14 X15 ;
genr ut = uhat
genr ut1 = ut(-1)
genr ut2 = ut(-2)
genr ut3 = ut(-3)
genr ut4 = ut(-4)
```

```
smpl 5 ;
ols ut const ut1 ut2 ut3 ut4 X2 X1 X3 X4 X5 X6
 X7 X8 X9 X10 X11 X12 X13 X14 X15 ;
genr LM = $nrsq
pvalue 3 4 LM
smpl 1 ;
ar 1 2 3 4 ; l_Y const l_X1 X3 X4 X5 X6 X7 X8 X9 l_X10
   X11 l_X12 l_X13 l_X14 ;
ar 1 3 4 ; l_Y const l_X1 X3 X4 X5 X6 X7 X8 X9 l_X10
   X11 l_X12 l_X13 l_X14 ;
omit X8 l_X10 l_X12 ;
omit X3 X7 l_X14 ;
```

Although the question asks for monthly dummies, they are not included here because the data are weekly and would have only four observations for each month. This is not adequate enough to pick up monthly differentials. The LM test statistic for AR(4) is 24.953 with a p-value less than 0.0001. Thus, generalized CORC is the appropriate estimation procedure. The estimates and associated statistics for the final model are given below.

VARIABLE	COEFFICIENT	STDERROR	T STAT	PROB t > |T|
constant	6.609948	0.660776	10.003311	< 0.0001 ***
l_X1	0.200461	0.06407	3.128795	0.002765 ***
X4	0.047725	0.022719	2.100618	0.04011 **
X5	0.065291	0.022633	2.884837	0.005519 ***
X6	0.108904	0.025308	4.303206	< 0.0001 ***
X9	0.148518	0.034552	4.298365	< 0.0001 ***
X11	-0.016913	0.009416	-1.796225	0.077759 *
l_X13	-0.381205	0.146481	-2.60243	0.011777 **

COVARIANCE MATRIX OF REGRESSION COEFFICIENTS

18) l_X1	5) X4	6) X5	7) X6	10) X9	
0.004105	-3.434670e-04	1.559159e-04	-8.663458e-04	-2.578572e-04	(18
	5.161673e-04	-1.678467e-04	6.809680e-05	5.683221e-05	(5
		5.122305e-04	-4.514194e-05	3.431656e-05	(6
			6.404737e-04	1.101663e-05	(7
				0.001194	(10

```
      12) X11        21) l_X13         0) const

 3.039271e-05   7.097038e-05       -0.002249     (18
 1.531069e-05  -2.396588e-04    3.400024e-04     (5
 8.817468e-07  -4.724212e-04    2.468075e-04     (6
-8.397441e-06   5.695002e-04    5.663721e-05     (7
 1.041490e-05      -0.001739        0.001345     (10
 8.865415e-05  -8.802500e-05    4.176127e-05     (12
                    0.021457       -0.015262     (21
                                    0.012055     (0

ESTIMATES OF THE AR COEFFICIENTS

ut_1                 0.37905      0.112294     3.375514     0.001276 ***
ut_3                0.245137        0.1179     2.079194     0.041742 **
ut_4                0.209649      0.121874     1.720207     0.090383 *
```

For testing the elasticities, only X1 and X13 are relevant. The test statistics are

$$t_c \text{ for X1} = \frac{1 - 0.200461}{0.06407} = 12.479$$

$$t_c \text{ for X13} = \frac{1 - 0.381205}{0.146481} = 4.224$$

Both these are high and significant and therefore we conclude that the elasticities are not unitary. Because they are both numerically less than one, they are inelastic.

EX 9.24

Use the following ESL commands to obtain the empirical results for this exercise.

```
genr dummy
ols volume const dummy_2 dummy_3 dummy_4 dummy_5 dummy_6
 dummy_7 dummy_8 dummy_9 dummy_10 dummy_11 dummy_12 sp500
 tbill long gdp cconf cexpect csent ;
genr ut = uhat
lags ut ;
smpl 1981.01 ;
ols ut const dummy_2 dummy_3 dummy_4 dummy_5 dummy_6 dummy_7
 dummy_8 dummy_9 dummy_10 dummy_11 dummy_12 sp500 tbill long
 gdp cconf cexpect csent ut_1 ut_2 ut_3 ut_4 ut_5 ut_6 ut_7
 ut_8 ut_9 ut_10 ut_11 ut_12 ;
```

```
genr LM = $nrsq
pvalue 3 12 LM
smpl 1980.01 ;
ar 1 2 3 4 5 6 7 8 9 10 11 12 ;
volume const dummy_2 dummy_3 dummy_4 dummy_5 dummy_6
 dummy_7 dummy_8 dummy_9 dummy_10 dummy_11 dummy_12
 sp500 tbill long gdp cconf cexpect csent ;
ar 1 2 3 5 6 7 8 9 11 ;
volume const dummy_2 dummy_3 dummy_4 dummy_5 dummy_6
 dummy_7 dummy_8 dummy_9 dummy_10 dummy_11 dummy_12
 sp500 tbill long gdp cconf cexpect csent ;
ar 1 2 3 5 9 11 ;
volume const dummy_2 dummy_3 dummy_4 dummy_5 dummy_6
 dummy_7 dummy_8 dummy_9 dummy_10 dummy_11 dummy_12
 sp500 tbill long gdp cconf cexpect csent ;
ar 1 2 3 9 11 ;
volume const dummy_2 dummy_3 dummy_4 dummy_5 dummy_6
 dummy_7 dummy_8 dummy_9 dummy_10 dummy_11 dummy_12
 sp500 tbill long gdp cconf cexpect csent ;
ar 1 2 3 9 ;
volume const dummy_2 dummy_3 dummy_4 dummy_5 dummy_6
 dummy_7 dummy_8 dummy_9 dummy_10 dummy_11 dummy_12
 sp500 tbill long gdp cconf cexpect csent ;
omit gdp ;
omit csent ;
omit long ;
omit dummy_3 ;
omit dummy_10 ;
```

The LM test statistic for AR(12) is 86.613 whose *p*-value is less than 0.01 percent. Because this is very small, generalized CORC is the appropriate estimation procedure. We estimated such a model using the most general formulation first. We then used data based model reduction. The final model had an adjusted R^2 of 0.946. Only the AR coefficients for the lags 1, 2, 3, and 9 were significant. Also, all the monthly dummy variables except those for March and October were significant (January dummy was excluded to avoid the dummy variable trap). Among the quantitative variables, only the coefficients for sp500, tbill, cconf, and cexpect were significant (at levels below 7 percent).

EX 9.25

The ESL commands for this exercise are too numerous to list here and are in the file *ex9-25.esl* available from the author.

The LM test statistic for AR(12) is 41.232 and the corresponding p-value is less than 0.0001 indicating that AR(12) is very significant. Therefore, generalized CORC is the appropriate estimation procedure. We estimated such a model using the most general formulation first. We then used data based model reduction. The final model had an adjusted R^2 of 0.997 which is extremely high. Only the AR coefficients for the lags 1, 2, 9, and 12 were significant. Interestingly none of the monthly dummy variables were significant (January dummy was excluded to avoid the dummy variable trap). Among the quantitative variables, only the elasticities for per capita income, unemployment rate, new car price index, insurance price index, public transportation price index, and installment credit were significant (see the table below). Income, unemployment rate, and the new car price index had the expected positive coefficients but the signs for insurance price, public transportation price index, and the consumer credit were counterintuitive.

VARIABLE	COEFFICIENT	STDERROR	T STAT	2Prob(t > |T|)
constant	-1.194026	0.284346	-4.199198	< 0.0001 ***
l_pcdpy	0.199588	0.118835	1.679529	0.094756 *
l_unempr	-0.08959	0.024337	-3.681222	0.000305 ***
l_rlnewp	-0.251468	0.109927	-2.287593	0.023305 **
l_rlinsp	0.483465	0.039185	12.337867	< 0.0001 ***
l_rltran	-0.121162	0.051161	-2.368226	0.018916 **
l_pccred	0.285362	0.031798	8.974171	< 0.0001 ***
ESTIMATES OF THE AR COEFFICIENTS				
ut_1	0.635125	0.071044	8.939924	< 0.0001 ***
ut_2	0.129605	0.069505	1.86469	0.0638 *
ut_9	-0.122446	0.049519	-2.47269	0.014308 **
ut_12	0.076727	0.044836	1.711291	0.088694 *

R-squared is computed as the square of the corr. between observed and predicted dep. var.

Unadjusted R-squared 0.997 Adjusted R-squared 0.997

CHAPTER 10

PRACTICE PROBLEMS

PP 10.1

To get the long run multiplier set $Y_t = Y^*$ and $X_t = X^*$ for all t. $Y^* = \alpha + \beta_0 X^* + \beta_0 \lambda X^* + \ldots = \alpha + \beta_0 X^*(1 + \lambda + \lambda^2 + \ldots) = \alpha + [\beta_0 X^*/(1-\lambda)]$. The long-run multiplier is $\Delta Y^*/\Delta X^* = \beta_0/(1-\lambda)$.

PP 10.2

Use the following ESL commands for the empirical results.

```
genr temp1=temp(-1)
genr temp2=temp(-2)
genr temp3=temp(-3)
genr temp4=temp(-4)
genr temp5=temp(-5)
genr temp6=temp(-6)
smpl 1.07 ;
ols load 0 temp temp1 temp2 temp3 temp4 temp5 temp6 ;
```

Adjusted R^2 is 0.059 which is considerably less than that for a model with a lagged dependent variable. The long-run multiplier is the sum of the coefficients for the temperature variables and is -18.504.

PP 10.3

The relevant equations are obtained by setting $\alpha_3 = 0$ in the Almon lag equations. The model now becomes

$$\begin{aligned} Y_t = \alpha &+ \alpha_0(X_t + X_{t-1} + X_{t-2} + X_{t-3} + X_{t-4}) \\ &+ \alpha_1(X_{t-1} + 2X_{t-2} + 3X_{t-3} + 4X_{t-4}) \\ &+ \alpha_2(X_{t-1} + 4X_{t-2} + 9X_{t-3} + 16X_{t-4}) + u_t \end{aligned}$$

The procedure is to generate the variables in parentheses and to use these as independent variables.

PP 10.4

We have $\beta_1 = 1 - \lambda$ and $\beta_2 = \beta\lambda$ from which we get $\hat{\lambda} = 1 - \hat{\beta}_1 = 1 - 0.667 = 0.333, \hat{\beta} = \hat{\beta}_2 / \hat{\lambda} = 0.3/0.333 = 0.9$. The marginal effect of sales on desired inventories is $\hat{\beta} = 0.9$. The marginal effect on actual sales is $\hat{\beta}_2 = 0.3$. The average number of periods is $1/\hat{\lambda} = 3$.

PP 10.5

The impact multiplier is $\Delta Y_t / \Delta X_t = 0$ and the long-run multiplier is $\hat{\beta} = 0.9$. The interim multiplier for one period is $\Delta \hat{Y}_t / \Delta X_{t-1} = \hat{\beta}_2 = 0.3$. For two periods, $Y_t = \beta_0 + \beta_1 (\beta_0 + \beta_1 Y_{t-2} + \beta_2 X_{t-2} + v_{t-1}) + \beta_2 X_{t-1} + v_t$. Hence $\Delta \hat{Y}_t / \Delta X_{t-2} = \hat{\beta}_1 \hat{\beta}_2 = 0.2$. For three periods, $\Delta \hat{Y}_t / \Delta X_{t-3} = \hat{\beta}_1^2 \hat{\beta}_2 = 0.133$, and for four periods it is $\hat{\beta}_1^3 \hat{\beta}_2 = 0.089$.

PP 10.6

If $u_t = (1-\lambda) u_{t-1} + \varepsilon_t$, from equation (10.17)

$$Y_t = \alpha\lambda + (1-\lambda) Y_{t-1} + \lambda\beta X_{t-1} + \varepsilon_t = \beta_0 + \beta_1 Y_{t-1} + \beta_2 X_{t-1} + \varepsilon_t$$

Because ε_t is white noise, OLS estimates of β_0, β_1, and β_2 are BLUE. Since $\lambda = 1 - \beta$, the OLS estimate of λ is BLUE (Gauss-Markov Theorem) but $\hat{\alpha}$ and $\hat{\beta}$ are nonlinear functions of β_0, β_1, and β_2. The BLUE property does not extend to nonlinear functions.

PP 10.7

The ESL commands for obtaining the empirical results are given below.

```
genr time
logs uswage calwage ;
lags l_uswage l_calwag;
genr dluswage = diff(l_uswage)
genr dlcalwag = diff(l_calwag)
lags dluswage dlcalwag ;
smpl 1962 ;
ols dluswage 0 time l_uswa_1 dluswa_1 ;
omit time l_uswa_1 ;
ols dlcalwag 0 time l_calw_1 dlcalw_1 ;
omit time l_calw_1 ;
smpl 1960 ;
```

```
ols l_calwag 0 l_uswage;
genr ut = uhat
genr ut1 = ut(-1)
genr diffut = diff(ut)
genr diffut_1 = diffut(-1)
genr diffut_2 = diffut(-2)
genr diffut_3 = diffut(-3)
genr diffut_4 = diffut(-4)
smpl 1965 ;
ols diffut ut1 diffut_1 diffut_2 diffut_3 diffut_4 ;
```

The F-statistics for testing for random walks are 3.473 and 1.632 respectively for the U.S. and California. As for the linear case, we cannot reject the null hypothesis of random walk. For the augmented Dickey-Fuller test, the t-statistic is 1.745 in absolute value. We note from Table 10.10 that this is considerably less than the critical values and hence we cannot reject the null hypothesis of no cointegration. Thus, the results parallel the linear case.

EXERCISES

EX 10.2

a. Taking logarithms of the model we get

$$\ln Y_t = \alpha + \beta \ln X_t^* + u_t$$

Taking logarithms of the adaptive rule,

$$\ln X_t^* - \ln X_{t-1}^* = \gamma \ln X_{t-1} - \gamma \ln X_{t-1}^*$$

or

$$\ln X_t^* = \gamma \ln X_{t-1} + (1-\gamma) \ln X_{t-1}^*$$

From the model we have, $\ln X_t^* = (\ln Y_t - \alpha - u_t)/\beta$. Substituting this in the adaptive rule,

$$\frac{\ln Y_t - \alpha - u_t}{\beta} = \gamma \ln X_{t-1} + \frac{(1-\gamma)(\ln Y_{t-1} - \alpha - u_{t-1})}{\beta}$$

or

$$\ln Y_t = \alpha\gamma + (1-\gamma) \ln Y_{t-1} + \beta \gamma \ln X_{t-1} + u_t - (1-\gamma) u_{t-1}$$

$$= \beta_0 + \beta_1 \ln Y_{t-1} + \beta_2 \ln X_{t-1} + v_t$$

b. By Property 3.2, consistency requires that $E(v_t) = 0$, $E(v_t \ln Y_{t-1}) = 0$, and $E(v_t \ln X_{t-1}) = 0$.

c. Because the model has a lagged dependent variable, OLS estimates are biased.

d. If u_t is normally distributed with the specified properties, $\ln Y_{t-1}$ will be correlated with $u_t - (1-\gamma)u_{t-1}$ and hence Assumption 3.4 is violated. OLS estimates are therefore not consistent.

EX 10.3

a. Even if there are no sales (that is, $S_t = 0$), inventories (α) will be positive. If sales increase, we would expect desired inventories to increase also, and hence β is likely to be positive. If desired inventories exceed actual inventories, we would expect actual inventories to increase and hence λ is likely to be positive. Also $\beta < 1$ and $\lambda < 1$, as otherwise the model will be explosive.

b.

$$I_t = \lambda I^*_{t-1} + (1-\lambda)I_{t-1} + u_t = \lambda(\alpha + \beta S_{t-1}) + (1-\lambda)I_{t-1} + u_t$$

$$= \lambda\alpha + \lambda\beta S_{t-1} + (1-\lambda)I_{t-1} + u_t = \beta_0 + \beta_1 S_{t-1} + \beta_2 I_{t-1} + u_t$$

c. For consistency we need $E(u_t) = 0$, $E(u_t S_{t-1}) = 0$ and $E(u_t I_{t-1}) = 0$, and the variances of S_t and I_t must be finite (see Property 3.2). These are not, however, enough for BLUE because the model has a lagged dependent variable.

d. α, β, and λ are estimable. First regress I_t against a constant, S_{t-1}, and I_{t-1} and get $\hat\beta_0$, $\hat\beta_1$, and $\hat\beta_2$. Then $\hat\lambda = 1 - \hat\beta_2$, $\hat\alpha = \hat\beta_0 / \hat\lambda$, and $\hat\beta = \hat\beta_1 / \hat\lambda$.

EX 10.5

a. By an argument similar to that in Exercise 10.3, $\alpha > 0$ and $0 < \beta, \lambda, \mu < 1$.

b.

$$S^*_t = \alpha + \beta Y^*_t$$

$$S_t = \lambda S^*_{t-1} + (1-\lambda) S_{t-1}$$

$$Y^*_t = \mu Y_{t-1} + (1-\mu) Y^*_{t-1}$$

From the first and second equations, $S_t = \lambda(\alpha + \beta Y^*_{t-1}) + (1-\lambda) S_{t-1}$. This implies that

$$Y^*_{t-1} = \frac{S_t - \lambda\alpha - (1-\lambda) S_{t-1}}{\lambda\beta}$$

From this and the third equation

$$\frac{S_{t+1} - \lambda\alpha - (1-\lambda)S_t}{\lambda\beta} = \mu Y_{t-1} + (1-\mu)\frac{S_t - \lambda\alpha - (1-\lambda)S_{t-1}}{\lambda\beta}$$

or

$$S_{t+1} - \lambda\alpha - (1-\lambda)S_t = \lambda\beta\mu Y_{t-1} + (1-\mu)[S_t - \lambda\alpha - (1-\lambda)S_{t-1})]$$

Rearranging terms, using t instead of t+1, and adding u_t,

$$\begin{aligned} S_t &= \lambda\alpha + (1-\lambda)S_{t-1} + \lambda\beta\mu Y_{t-2} + (1-\mu)S_{t-1} \\ &\quad - \lambda\alpha(1-\mu) - (1-\mu)(1-\lambda)S_{t-2} + u_t \\ &= \lambda\alpha\mu + \lambda\beta\mu Y_{t-2} + (2-\lambda-\mu)S_{t-1} - (1-\mu)(1-\lambda)S_{t-2} + u_t \\ &= \beta_0 + \beta_1 Y_{t-2} + \beta_2 S_{t-1} + \beta_3 S_{t-2} + u_t \end{aligned}$$

c. The conditions for consistency are $E(u_t) = E(u_t Y_{t-2}) = E(u_t S_{t-1}) = E(u_t S_{t-2}) = 0$. The estimates are biased because of the presence of two lagged endogenous variables and therefore are not BLUE.

d. We have $\beta_0 = \lambda\alpha\mu$, $\beta_1 = \lambda\beta\mu$, $\beta_2 = 2-\lambda-\mu$, and $\beta_3 = -(1-\mu)(1-\lambda)$. Let $\lambda_0 = 1-\lambda$ and $\mu_0 = 1-\mu$. The last two equations may be written as $\lambda_0 + \mu_0 = \beta_2$ and $\lambda_0\mu_0 = -\beta_3$. From these, $(\lambda_0 - \mu_0)^2 = (\lambda_0 + \mu_0)^2 - 4\lambda_0\mu_0 = \beta_2^2 + 4\beta_3$, or $(\lambda_0 - \mu_0) = \pm(\beta_2^2 + 4\beta_3)^{½}$. λ and μ are solved from these as

$$\lambda = 1 - \frac{1}{2}\left[\beta_2 \pm (\beta_2^2 + 4\beta_3)^{½}\right]$$

$$\mu = 1 - \frac{1}{2}\left[\beta_2 \pm (\beta_2^2 + 4\beta_3)^{½}\right]$$

It will be noted that the solutions may not be unique or will not exist unless $\beta_2^2 + 4\beta_3 \geq 0$.

EX 10.6

The following commands would be useful in obtaining the necessary output to answer this question.

```
genr Yt1 = Yt(-1)
genr Yt2 = Yt(-2)
genr Yt3 = Yt(-3)
genr Yt4 = Yt(-4)
genr Yt5 = Yt(-5)
```

```
genr Yt6 = Yt(-6)
(*  suppress the first 6 observations  *)
smpl 1965 ;
corr Yt Yt1 Yt2 Yt3 Yt4 Yt5 Yt6;
ols Ct 0 Yt Yt1 Yt2 Yt3 Yt4 Yt5 Yt6;
(*  LM test for AR(1)  *)
genr ut = uhat
genr ut1 = ut(-1)
smpl 1966 ;
ols ut 0 ut1 Yt Yt1 Yt2 Yt3 Yt4 Yt5 Yt6;
genr LM = $trsq
pvalue 3 1 LM
(*  reset start date to 1965 and use mixed HILU-CORC  *)
smpl 1965 ;
hilu Ct 0 Yt Yt1 Yt2 Yt3 Yt4 Yt5 Yt6;
genr temp = coeff(Yt) + coeff(Yt1) + coeff(Yt2) + coeff(Yt3)
genr mult =  temp + coeff(Yt4) + coeff(Yt5) + coeff(Yt6)
print mult;
```

As may be expected, there is a great deal of multicollinearity among the explanatory variables with pairwise correlations 0.987 or higher. As a result, most of the coefficients are insignificant with the exception of that for *Yt*. This result holds even though the LM test for first-order autocorrelation indicated significance and the model was reestimated with the mixed HILU-CORC method. The long-run multiplier is the sum of the coefficients for the *Y* terms and is almost 1.

EX 10.7

The relevant model for this is given in equation (10.10). The commands for obtaining the empirical results are as follows.

```
genr Ct1 = Ct(-1)
genr Yt1 = Yt(-1)
corr Ct1 Yt1 ;
(*  suppress the first observation  *)
smpl 1960 ;
ols Ct 0 Ct1 Yt1 ;
(*  LM test for AR(1)  *)
```

```
genr ut = uhat
genr ut1 = ut(-1)
smpl 1961 ;
ols ut 0 ut1 Ct1 Yt1 ;
genr LM = $trsq
pvalue 3 1 LM
(* reset start date to 1960 and use mixed HILU-CORC *)
smpl 1960 ;
hilu Ct 0 Ct1 Yt1 ;
```

The LM test for first-order serial correlation indicates its presence and hence the mixed HILU-CORC procedure is appropriate. The estimates and associated statistics are presented below.

VARIABLE	COEFFICIENT	STDERROR	T STAT	2Prob(t > |T|)
constant	29685.821458	7271.688824	4.082383	0.00029 ***
Ct1	0.725975	0.264336	2.746412	0.009942 ***
Yt1	-0.438702	0.246785	-1.777668	0.085271 *

Adjusted R^2, computed as the square of the correlation between observed and predicted dependent variable is 0.995. The estimates of the original model are given by $\hat{\lambda} = 1 - \hat{\beta}_2 = 1 - 0.726 = 0.274$. $\hat{\alpha} = \hat{\beta}_1 / \hat{\lambda} = 29686/0.274 = 108{,}343$. $\hat{\beta} = \hat{\beta}_3 / \hat{\lambda} = -0.439/0.274 = -1.602$. The estimates are nonsensical and unacceptable, especially the large negative value for the marginal propensity to consume out of expected income. Two possible reasons are (1) high multicollinearity between $Ct1$ and $Yt1$ and (2) the fact that there might be a feedback effect from consumption to income which causes estimates to be biased (more on this in Chapter 13).

EX 10.8

For the empirical analysis of this question use the same data file and the following ESL commands.

```
genr time
genr lnCt1 = ln(Ct(-1))
(* generate first difference in the log as in equation (10.21) *)
genr DCt = ldiff(Ct)
genr DCt1 = DCt(-1)
genr DCt2 = DCt(-2)
```

```
genr DCt3 = DCt(-3)
genr DCt4 = DCt(-4)
genr DCt5 = DCt(-5)
genr DCt6 = DCt(-6)
(* estimate the Dickey-Fuller test regression *)
smpl 1966 ;
ols DCt 0 time lnCt1 DCt1 DCt2 DCt3 DCt4 DCt5 DCt6 ;
omit time lnCt1 ;
(* Redo analysis with Yt instead of Ct *)
smpl 1959 ;
genr lnYt1 = ln(Yt(-1))
genr DYt = ldiff(Yt)
genr DYt1 = DYt(-1)
genr DYt2 = DYt(-2)
genr DYt3 = DYt(-3)
genr DYt4 = DYt(-4)
genr DYt5 = DYt(-5)
genr DYt6 = DYt(-6)
(* estimate the Dickey-Fuller test regression *)
smpl 1966 ;
ols DYt 0 time lnYt1 DYt1 DYt2 DYt3 DYt4 DYt5 DYt6 ;
omit time lnYt1 ;
```

The unrestricted model for the unit root test is given by equation (10.21). *F*-statistics for the Dickey-Fuller test are given as 3.29 for consumption and as 3.564 for income. From Table 10.7 we note that the test statistics are below the critical values for levels at or below 10 percent. Thus unit root cannot be rejected in either case. A modified model could be the error correction model described in Section 10.8 and carried out in the next exercise.

EX 10.9

The relevant ESL commands for the error correction model are given below.

```
genr LDCt = ldiff(Ct)
genr LDYt = ldiff(Yt)
genr LY_C = ln(Yt(-1)) - ln(Ct(-1))
smpl 1960 ;
ols LDCt 0 LDYt LY_C ;
```

The short-run adjustment coefficient is 0.214 with a p-value of 0.095 which is significant at the 10 percent level.

EX 10.10
The relevant ESL commands are as follows.

```
genr time
(* generate first difference in the log as in equation (10.21) *)
genr lnpop1 = ln(pop(-1))
genr Dpop = ldiff(pop)
genr Dpop1 = Dpop(-1)
genr Dpop2 = Dpop(-2)
genr Dpop3 = Dpop(-3)
genr Dpop4 = Dpop(-4)
genr Dpop5 = Dpop(-5)
genr Dpop6 = Dpop(-6)
(* estimate the Dickey-Fuller test regression *)
smpl 1967 ;
ols Dpop 0 time lnpop1 Dpop1 Dpop2 Dpop3 Dpop4 Dpop5 Dpop6 ;
omit time lnpop1 ;
```

The F-statistic for the Dickey-Fuller test for unit root is given by 2.174 which is not significant even at the 10 percent level. The presence of a unit root is therefore suggested.

EX 10.11
The following ESL commands will be useful in carrying out the empirical analysis for this.

```
genr time
genr Yt = farmpop
genr Yt1 =Yt(-1)
genr Yt2 =Yt(-2)
smpl 1950 ;
ols Yt 0 Yt1 Yt2 time ;
genr ua = uhat
ols Yt 0 Yt1 Yt2 ;
smpl 1949 ;
```

```
ols Yt 0 Yt1 time;
genr ub = uhat
ols Yt 0 Yt1 ;
lags ua ub;
smpl 1951 ;
ols ua 0 Yt1 Yt2 time ua_1 ;
genr LM1 = $trsq
pvalue 3 1 LM1
smpl 1950 ;
ols ub 0 Yt1 time ub_1 ;
genr LM2 = $trsq
pvalue 3 1 LM2
```

In terms of the model selection statistics, the first model (call it Model A) with two lags is better than the second one (Model B) and a third one in which the *time* variable is omitted). The Durbin-h test is applicable only for Model B. The test statistic is (see Section 10.2)

$$h = \hat{\rho}\left[\frac{n'}{1-n's_{\hat{\beta}}^2}\right]^{1/2}$$

where $\hat{\rho}$ is the first order autocorrelation, $n' = 43$, and $s_{\hat{\beta}}$ is the standard error for the coefficient of Y_{t-1}. For Model B, $n' = 43, \hat{\rho} = -0.193, s_{\hat{\beta}} = 0.027084$, and hence $h = -1.29$. From Table A.1 we see that the area to the right of 1.29 in the standard normal distribution is 0.0985 (0.5 - 0.4015) > 0.05 and hence there no significant serial correlation in the second model at the 5 percent level.

The LM test statistics for the two models are, respectively, 4.299 and 2.421. From the p-values it is easy to verify that this statistics is significant for Model A at the 5 percent level but not for Model B, thus supporting the Durbin-h test. Because serial correlation is present and there are lagged endogenous variables, OLS estimates of Model A are not consistent but those of Model B are.

EX 10.12

a. From Chapter 6, multicollinearity makes standard errors larger, but estimates are still unbiased, consistent, and most efficient (BLUE). Ignoring serial correlation, however, makes estimates inefficient. Similarly, adding an irrelevant variables also makes estimates inefficient. The results are thus not similar (that is, the statement is false).

b. Model B has Y_{t-1} which is generally highly correlated with Y_t. We would therefore expect it to have a higher R^2 than Model A (that is, the statement is true).

c. We saw in Section 10.2 that the presence of a lagged dependent variable generally results in a higher DW statistic (d) than one without the lagged variable. If even this higher d is less than d_L, serial correlation is indicated. The statement is therefore true.

EX 10.13

The empirical results for this exercise can be obtained by using the following ESL commands.

```
logs Q Y P ED1 ED2 ;
genr LQ1 = l_Q(-1)
smpl 1961 ;
(* Estimate partial adjustment model *)
ols l_Q const LQ1 l_Y l_P ED1 ED2 D82 D86 ;
(* Save the residuals *)
genr ut = uhat
(* Generate lag terms *)
genr ut1=ut(-1)
genr ut2=ut(-2)
(* Reset sample and estimate auxiliary regression for AR(1) *)
smpl 1963 ;
ols ut const ut1 ut2 LQ1 l_Y l_P ED1 ED2 D82 D86 ;
(* Compute LM test statistic and its p-value *)
genr LM = $trsq
pvalue 3 2 LM
smpl 1961 ;
ar 1 2 ; l_Q const LQ1 l_Y l_P ED1 ED2 D82 D86 ;
omit D86 ;
omit ED1 ;
```

The LM test statistic for AR(2) is 5.557691 and the corresponding p-value is 0.06211. We then used the generalized CORC and eliminated insignificant variables. The final model estimates are given below.

VARIABLE	COEFFICIENT	STDERROR	T STAT	PROB t > |T|
constant	-3.531397	0.830864	-4.250272	0.000392 ***
LQ1	0.456747	0.108725	4.200944	0.00044 ***
l_Y	0.503805	0.116218	4.335008	0.000321 ***
l_P	-0.176886	0.079895	-2.213973	0.038612 **
ED2	-1.20041	0.605325	-1.983085	0.06126 *
D82	-0.108553	0.019257	-5.637175	< 0.0001 ***
ESTIMATES OF THE AR COEFFICIENTS				
ut_1	-0.321306	0.179959	-1.785441	0.086835 *
ut_2	-0.437914	0.18144	-2.413543	0.023793 **
Unadjusted R-squared	0.901	Adjusted R-squared		0.876

The long-run income elasticity is given by 0.503805/(1 – 0.456747) = 0.927 and the price elasticity is given by – 0.176886/(1 – 0.456747) = – 0.326. Both elasticities make sense. Cigarette demand is both price and income inelastic.

EX 10.14

The ESL commands useful in obtaining the necessary empirical results are included in the disk under the file *esl10-14.esl.*

From Section 10.1 the partial adjustment mechanism yields the lagged dependent variable Y_{t-1}. Inclusion of this variable in the model does not improve the model. Most of the model selection statistics are worse and hence this model is not to be preferred over the one in Exercise 9.16.

EX 10.15

The relevant ESL commands are too numerous to reproduce here. They are in the disk in the file *ex10-15.esl.* The model exhibited both seasonal effects and higher-order serial correlation. The final model estimates using the generalized Cochrane-Orcutt procedure are given below.

VARIABLE	COEFFICIENT	STDERROR	T STAT	2Prob(t > |T|)
constant	-0.676669	0.123732	-5.468842	< 0.0001 ***
lPCSTOK1	0.462162	0.088737	5.208237	< 0.0001 ***
FALL	0.086879	0.023079	3.764445	0.00044 ***
ln(PRICE)	0.077174	0.015052	5.12724	< 0.0001 ***

SUMMER x ln(PRICE)	-0.027503	0.005366	-5.125408	< 0.0001	***
SUMMER x ln(INCOME)	0.053528	0.010375	5.159282	< 0.0001	***
FALL x ln(INCOME)	-0.029621	0.007935	-3.733058	0.000485	***
ln(UNEMP)	-0.041897	0.008014	-5.227859	< 0.0001	***
FALL x ln(UNEMP)	-0.008162	0.003199	-2.551128	0.013844	**
ESTIMATES OF THE AR COEFFICIENTS					
ut_1	0.611748	0.120821	5.063252	< 0.0001	***
ut_2	0.481112	0.149676	3.214364	0.002171	***
ut_4	-0.38767	0.101541	-3.817886	0.000339	***

R-squared is computed as the square of the corr. between observed and predicted dep. var.

Unadjusted R-squared 0.994 Adjusted R-squared 0.993

EX 10.16

a. Taking logarithms we get $\ln P_t = \ln K + \ln M_t - \ln N_t$ or $p_t = k + m_t - n_t$. This gives $\Delta p_t = \Delta m_t - \Delta n_t$.

b. $p_t = \beta_0 + \beta_1 p_{t-1} + \beta_2 m_t + \beta_3 m_{t-1} + \beta_4 n_t + \beta_5 n_{t-1} + u_t$. Substitute $\beta_1 = 1-\gamma$, $\beta_3 = \gamma - \beta_2$, and $\beta_5 = -\gamma - \beta_4$. We have,

$$p_t = \beta_0 + (1-\gamma)p_{t-1} + \beta_2 m_t + (\gamma - \beta_2)m_{t-1} + \beta_4 n_t - (\gamma + \beta_4)\, n_{t-1} + u_t$$

which gives

$$\Delta p_t = \beta_0 + \beta_2 \Delta m_t + \beta_4 \Delta n_t - \gamma(p_{t-1} - m_{t-1} + n_{t-1}) + u_t$$

In the long run, the change in variables is zero. This reduces to $p^* = k_0 + m^* - n^*$, which is of the form in part (a).

c. The model derived in part (b) is the error-correction model. If $\gamma \neq 0$ there is support for the error-correction mechanism. The empirical results may be obtained with the following ESL commands and the data file DATA10-6.

```
lags N M P;
genr DN = diff(N)
genr DM = diff(M)
genr DP = diff(P)
genr Z = P_1 - M_1 + N_1
smpl 1960 ;
ols DP 0 DM DN Z;
omit DN;
```

We note that $\hat{\gamma}$ is significantly different from zero. Thus there is support for the error-correction mechanism. It is interesting that only the money supply term (besides the error-correction term) is statistically significant. Change in population does not appear to matter in explaining changes in the price level.

EX 10.17

The following ESL commands will be useful to obtain the empirical results for this question.

```
genr ml=um*100/gnpdef
genr g=ug*100/gnpdef
genr time
lags ml g;
genr dml = diff(ml)
genr dg = diff(g)
lags dml dg ;
smpl 1942 ;
ols dml 0 time ml_1 dml_1 ;
omit time ml_1 ;
ols dg 0 time g_1 dg_1 ;
omit time g_1 ;
smpl 1940 ;
ols ml 0 g;
genr ut = uhat
genr ut1 = ut(-1)
genr diffut = diff(ut)
genr diffut_1 = diffut(-1)
genr diffut_2 = diffut(-2)
genr diffut_3 = diffut(-3)
genr diffut_4 = diffut(-4)
smpl 1945 ;
ols diffut ut1 diffut_1 diffut_2 diffut_3 diffut_4 ;
```

F-statistics for the Dickey-Fuller test for unit roots are 22.913 and 10.820 for military and total government expenditures. We see from Table 10.4 that these values are significant at the 1 percent level. Thus we reject the null hypothesis of unit root.

From the cointegration regression, the DW statistic is 0.377 which is significant at the 10 percent level but not at the 5 percent level (see Table 11.8). The t-statistic for $\hat{u}_{t-1}$ in the Dickey-Fuller regression is 2.867 in absolute value. This too is significant at the 10 percent level but not at the 5 percent level. Thus, there is some evidence of cointegration, but it is not very strong.

EX 10.18

Analysis for the U.S. Data

The following ESL commands will be useful to obtain the empirical results using the U.S. consumption and income data in DATA3-6.

```
genr ct = Ct - mean(Ct)
genr yt = Yt - mean(Yt)
genr ct1 = ct(-1)
genr yt1 = yt(-1)
genr ct2 = ct(-2)
genr yt2 = yt(-2)
genr ct3 = ct(-3)
genr yt3 = yt(-3)
genr ct4 = ct(-4)
genr yt4 = yt(-4)
(* F-tests for Granger-causality *)
smpl 1963 ;
ols ct 0 ct1 ct2 ct3 ct4 yt1 yt2 yt3 yt4 ;
omit yt1 yt2 yt3 yt4 ;
ols yt 0 yt1 yt2 yt3 yt4 ct1 ct2 ct3 ct4 ;
omit ct1 ct2 ct3 ct4 ;
(* DW test for cointegration *)
smpl 1959 ;
ols Ct 0 Yt ;
(* Augmented Dickey-Fuller test *)
genr ut = uhat
genr ut1 = ut(-1)
genr dut = diff(ut)
genr dut1 = dut(-1)
genr dut2 = dut(-2)
genr dut3 = dut(-3)
```

```
genr dut4 = dut(-4)
smpl 1964 ;
ols dut ut1 dut1 dut2 dut3 dut4 ;
```

The F-statistic for causality from income to consumption is 1.609 and its p-value is 0.206. Even at the 10 percent we cannot reject the null hypothesis of no causality. In contrast, the F-statistic for causality from consumption to income is 4.142 with a p-value of 0.011. There is thus significant causal effects from consumption to income but the feedback is weak, if at all present.

The DW test statistic for cointegration is 0.514, which is higher than the critical values for the 5 and 10 percent levels presented n Table 10.10. This supports the hypothesis that the two series are cointegrated. The augmented Dickey-Fuller test statistic is -1.26 which is numerically less than those in Table 10.10. Thus this test does not support cointegration.

Analysis for the U.K. Data

The following ESL commands will be useful to obtain the empirical results using the U.K. consumption and income data in DATA6-3.

```
genr Ct = Cons
genr Yt = DI
genr ct = Ct - mean(Ct)
genr yt = Yt - mean(Yt)
genr ct1 = ct(-1)
genr yt1 = yt(-1)
genr ct2 = ct(-2)
genr yt2 = yt(-2)
genr ct3 = ct(-3)
genr yt3 = yt(-3)
genr ct4 = ct(-4)
genr yt4 = yt(-4)
(* F-tests for Granger-causality *)
smpl 1952 ;
ols ct 0 ct1 ct2 ct3 ct4 yt1 yt2 yt3 yt4 ;
omit yt1 yt2 yt3 yt4 ;
ols yt 0 yt1 yt2 yt3 yt4 ct1 ct2 ct3 ct4 ;
omit ct1 ct2 ct3 ct4 ;
```

```
(* DW test for cointegration *)
smpl 1948 ;
ols Ct 0 Yt ;
(* Augmented Dickey-Fuller test *)
genr ut = uhat
genr ut1 = ut(-1)
genr dut = diff(ut)
genr dut1 = dut(-1)
genr dut2 = dut(-2)
genr dut3 = dut(-3)
genr dut4 = dut(-4)
smpl 1953 ;
ols dut ut1 dut1 dut2 dut3 dut4 ;
```

The F-statistic for causality from income to consumption is 3.383657 and its p-value is 0.021741 which implies significant causality. For the F-test for causality from consumption to income indicates the statistic of 4.469091 with a p-value of 0.006178. Thus there is a feedback effect here.

The DW test statistic for cointegration is 0.247444 which is below the values in Table 10.10. This test therefore does not support cointegration. For the augmented Dickey-Fuller test, the t-statistic is -1.509274 which is numerically below the values in Table 10.10. This test too does not support cointegration.

EX 10.19

The ESL commands for obtaining the empirical results are given below.

```
genr lmoney1 = lmoney(-1)
ols lmoney const lincome intrate ;
genr ut = uhat
genr ut1 = ut(-1)
genr ut2 = ut(-2)
genr ut3 = ut(-3)
smpl 1903 ;
ols ut const lincome intrate ut1 ut2 ut3 ;
genr LM1 = $nrsq
pvalue 3 3 LM1
smpl 1900 ;
```

```
ar 1 2 3 ; lmoney const lincome intrate ;
hilu lmoney const lincome intrate ;
smpl 1901 ;
ols lmoney const lmoney1 lincome intrate ;
genr utt = uhat
genr utt1 = utt(-1)
genr utt2 = utt(-2)
genr utt3 = utt(-3)
smpl 1904 ;
ols utt const lincome intrate utt1 utt2 utt3 ;
genr LM2 = $nrsq
pvalue 3 3 LM2
smpl 1901 ;
ar 1 2 3 ; lmoney const lmoney1 lincome intrate ;
ar 1 3 ; lmoney const lmoney1 lincome intrate ;
```

Both models exhibited significant serial correlation. The static model was reestimated by the mixed HILU-CORC method and the dynamic model was estimated by the generalized Cochrane-Orcutt procedure. In terms of the model selection statistics, the dynamic model was better. The estimated final model is given below. The long-run elasticities for income and interest rate are, respectively, 0.913 and -0.095.

VARIABLE	COEFFICIENT	STDERROR	T STAT	2Prob(t > |T|)	
constant	-0.097217	0.045358	-2.143314	0.035051	**
lmoney(-1)	0.82142	0.043154	19.034448	< 0.0001	***
lincome	0.163071	0.040073	4.069383	0.000108	***
intrate	-0.017384	0.003588	-4.844425	< 0.0001	***
ESTIMATES OF THE AR COEFFICIENTS					
ut_1	0.230761	0.103209	2.235861	0.028013	**
ut_3	0.237825	0.101585	2.341139	0.021594	**

R-squared is computed as the square of the corr. between observed and predicted dep. var.

Unadjusted R-squared 0.995 Adjusted R-squared 0.995

EX 10.20

Use the following ESL commands for the empirical results.

```
genr exrate1 = exrate(-1)
smpl 1982.2 ;
ols exrate const curracc trade m1_k m1_u irate_k irate_u pricek priceu
   exrate1 ;
genr ut = uhat
lags ut ;
smpl 1983.2 ;
ols exrate const curracc trade m1_k m1_u irate_k irate_u pricek priceu
   exrate1 ut_1 ut_2 ut_3 ut_4 ;
genr LM = $nrsq
pvalue 3 4 LM
smpl 1982.2 ;
ar 1 2 3 4 ;
exrate const curracc trade m1_k m1_u irate_k irate_u pricek priceu
   exrate1 ;
ar 2 3 4 ;
exrate const curracc trade m1_k m1_u irate_k irate_u pricek priceu
   exrate1 ;
omit 8 ;
```

The partial adjustment mechanism suggests using the lag exchange rate as an explanatory variable. The basic model was found to have significant AR(4) and hence was estimated by the generalized Cochrane-Orcutt procedure. The final model after omitting variables with insignificant coefficients is given below. The model explains 98.8 percent of the variation in the Korean exchange rate.

VARIABLE	COEFFICIENT	STDERROR	T STAT	2Prob(t > |T|)	
constant	57.746295	57.118411	1.010993	0.317949	
curracc	-0.024195	0.004265	-5.673336	< 0.0001	***
trade	0.021702	0.004983	4.355478	< 0.0001	***
m1_k	0.001321	6.152118e-04	2.147072	0.037751	**
m1_u	-0.066861	0.021748	-3.074311	0.003745	***
irate_k	-1.115325	0.562032	-1.984452	0.053926	*
pricek	-1.627522	0.609099	-2.672013	0.010768	**
priceu	1.647753	0.498967	3.30233	0.001994	***
exrate1	0.998815	0.022346	44.698495	< 0.0001	***

ESTIMATES OF THE AR COEFFICIENTS

ut_2	-0.352423	0.127285	-2.768766	0.008028	***
ut_3	-0.357545	0.122309	-2.923306	0.005313	***
ut_4	-0.228959	0.130178	-1.758811	0.085119	*

R-squared is computed as the square of the corr. between observed and predicted dep. var.

Unadjusted R-squared 0.990 Adjusted R-squared 0.988

CHAPTER 11

PRACTICE PROBLEMS

PP 11.1

While forecasting, u_t is set to zero because it is unpredictable. All the log models have the term $\hat{\sigma}^2/2$ to correct for the bias discussed in Section 11.4. The desired formulas are obtained by simply exponentiating the log models.

Log-linear: Whether $\hat{\beta}_1$ is positive, zero, or negative, the shape of the relation between $\hat{Y}_t$ and t is the same. If $\hat{\beta}_2 > 0$ the relationship is an exponentially increasing function starting at $e^{\hat{\beta}_1 + (\hat{\sigma}^2/2)}$. If $\hat{\beta}_2 < 0$ the graph will be exponentially decreasing to zero. If $\hat{\beta}_2 = 0$, we get a horizontal line.

Double-log: Here also the sign of $\hat{\beta}_2$ determines the shape. If $\hat{\beta}_2 = 0$ we have a horizontal line. The slope of the function is

$$\frac{d\hat{Y}_t}{dt} = e^{\hat{\beta}_1 + (\hat{\sigma}^2/2)} \hat{\beta}_2 t^{\hat{\beta}_2 - 1}$$

If $\hat{\beta}_2 > 1$ this slope is always positive. Hence $\hat{Y}_t$ steadily increases at an increasing rate. If $0 < \hat{\beta}_2 < 1$ then also $\hat{Y}_t$ increases, but at a decreasing rate. If $\hat{\beta}_2 < 0$, then $d\hat{Y}_t/dt$ is negative and hence $\hat{Y}_t$ steadily decreases to zero.

Logistic: If $\hat{\beta}_2 > 0$ the graph will be as in Figure 4.1. When $\hat{\beta}_2$ is negative, the shape will be a mirror image, decreasing steadily and with a point of inflection.

PP 11.2

Using the diskfile *pp11-2.esl* execute the DOS command

```
esl -v50 data10-5 < pp11-2.esl > pp11-2.out
```

For each of the forecasts, an equation of the form $Y_t = a + b\, Y_t^f$ was estimated as described in Section 11.2. If the forecast was perfect, we would expect a to be zero and b to 1. The following table summarizes the values of a and b and the corresponding $\bar{R}^2$ for the above regression.

Model	$\hat{a}$	$\hat{b}$	$\bar{R}^2$
A	0.21207	0.96532	0.993
B	- 1.06766	1.10318	0.992
C	13.68808	2.40314	0.997
D	- 0.17561	1.01717	0.992
E	- 0.153961	1.01893	0.992
F	1.75431	0.79151	0.993
G	0.13182	0.96264	0.992
H	0.30442	0.948238	0.994

Although the goodness of fit is excellent for out of sample performance, they all suffer from bias due to the fact that none of the values for a is near zero. The cubic model C has the best overall fit but it suffers from serious bias. In that dimension Models D and E are good.

PP 11.3

a. The first difference is

$$\Delta Y_t = Y_t - Y_{t-1} = \alpha + \beta t + \gamma t^2 - \alpha - \beta(t-1) - \gamma(t-1)^2 = \beta + \gamma(2t-1)$$

The second difference is therefore

$$\Delta^2 Y_t = \beta - \gamma + 2\gamma t - \left[(\beta - \gamma) + 2\gamma\,(t-1)\right] = 2\gamma$$

which is constant and is hence stationary.

(b) Let $Y_t = \alpha + \beta t$. Then

$$\Delta_i = Y_t - Y_{t-i} = \alpha + \beta t - \left[\alpha + \beta(t-i)\right] = \beta\, i$$

which is constant. Hence Δ_i is stationary.

EXERCISES

EX 11.1

Sections 11.1 and 11.3 have the appropriate definitions.

EX 11.2

See Section 11.2.

EX 11.3

The first step is to regress (using sample period data) actual Y_t against a constant, f_{t1}, f_{t2}, and f_{t3} and obtain the weights $\hat{\beta}_o, \hat{\beta}_1, \hat{\beta}_2$, and $\hat{\beta}_3$. Next obtain h-step ahead forecasts $f_{t+h,1}$, $f_{t+h,2}$, and $f_{t+h,3}$. The combined h-step ahead forecast is $f_{t+h} = \hat{\beta}_0 + \hat{\beta}_1 f_{t+h,1} + \hat{\beta}_2 f_{t+h,2} + \hat{\beta}_3 f_{t+h,3}$.

EX 11.4

Deseasonalizing refers to the process of removing the seasonal effects from a series. Define seasonal dummy variables D_1, D_2, and D_3 which take the value 1 during the first, second, and third quarters respectively, and 0 in other quarters. Next regress sales (S_t) against a constant, D_1, D_2, and D_3. The deseasonalized series is given by $S_t^* = S_t - \hat{\beta}_o - \hat{\beta}_1 D_1 - \hat{\beta}_2 D_2 - \hat{\beta}_3 D_3$, where the $\hat{\beta}$'s are the estimated regression coefficients.

EX 11.5

Detrending stands for the process of removing a time trend from a series. First graph Y_t against time and identify the shape of the relationship (see Section 11.4 for possible functional form). Let $f(t)$ be the fitted function. Then the detrended series is $Y_t^* = Y_t - f(t)$. For example if a quadratic relation was fit, the detrended series will be $Y_t^* = Y_t - \hat{\beta}_o - \hat{\beta}_1 t - \hat{\beta}_2 t^2$, where the $\hat{\beta}$'s are the estimated regression coefficients.

EX 11.7

$Var(u_t) = Var(\varepsilon_t - \lambda\varepsilon_{t-1}) = \sigma^2(1 + \lambda^2)$. $Cov(u_t, u_{t-1}) = Cov(\varepsilon_t - \lambda\varepsilon_{t-1}, \varepsilon_{t-1} - \lambda\varepsilon_{t-2}) = -\lambda\sigma^2$. Finally, $Cov(u_t, u_{t-s}) = 0$ for all $s > 1$ because ε_t is a white noise series. Therefore the only non-zero correlation is with $t-1$ for which the correlation coefficient is $-\lambda/(1 + \lambda^2)$. It is easy to extend this analysis to prove that if the moving average is of order p, the first p autocorrelation values will be non-zero but the rest will be zero.

EX 11.9

See Section 11.7 for the definition of *stationarity*.

Taking logarithms of both sides of the relation, $\ln(Y_t) = \ln(Y_o) + \lambda t$. First difference in logs is

$$\Delta\ln(Y_t) = \ln(Y_t) - \ln(Y_{t-1}) = \lambda$$

which is constant and hence is stationary.

EX 11.11

The first step is to decide on the differencing. Use the Ljung-Box test in equation (11.25) to check whether the series is stationary. If it is not, graph it against time. If the series exhibits a linear trend, difference once. If the trend is quadratic, difference twice. If the trend is exponential, take logarithms first and then difference. Test for stationarity at each stage. If seasonality is present, deseasonalize the series.

Next graph the correlogram. If it remains near zero after a certain lag, then that is the approximate choice for the moving average order. Then graph the partial correlogram. If it remains near zero after a certain lag, then that is the order of autoregression. If neither of these happens but both plots eventually decline to zero, start with an ARMA(1, 1) model.

The model is next estimated using a maximum likelihood estimation program. After estimating the model test whether the residual errors are white noise. The orders of autoregression and moving average can also be changed and the new model tested to see if it predicts better.

EX 11.12

The procedure is very much like the one adopted in Practice Problem 11.2.

CHAPTER 12

EXERCISES

EX 12.2

The ESL commands for this exercise are given below.

```
ols Accept const GPA Bio Chem Phy Red Prb Qnt Age Gender ;
genr yhat1=Accept-uhat
print yhat1 ;
genr d=(yhat1>0)*(yhat1<1)
genr sigmasq = yhat1*(1-yhat1)
genr wt=sqrt((1/sigmasq)*d)
wls wt Accept const GPA Bio Chem Phy Red Prb Qnt Age Gender ;
genr yhat2=Accept-uhat
print -o yhat1 d sigmasq wt yhat2 ;
```

We note that both OLS and WLS (after setting the weights to zero for the inadmissible cases) give some predictions outside the range [0, 1]. This empirically demonstrates the uselessness of the approach used by the linear probability model.

EX 12.4

The dependent variable is not binary here but is a fraction. Therefore the logit model would be more appropriate. First compute $Z = \ln[H/(1-H)]$ and regress Z against a constant, Y, P, and R.

EX 12.5

Since we want to know whether a particular employee joins the union or not, we would want to survey individual employees. However, we would also choose several companies and survey their employees. As in the application in Section 12.2 the logit model in equation (12.3) would be appropriate with a general maximum likelihood procedure. Several characteristics of the individual will be measured; age, gender, race, education, skill level or occupational status, income, and so on. Across companies some variables will differ; union membership fee, percentage of workers who are already union members, etc.

EX 12.6

The linear probability model or the logit model would be appropriate, but the logit model is preferable because of the problems that a linear probability model creates. Let P be the probability of conviction. For individual observations P will be 1 or 0. Equation (12.2) would be estimated because in equation (12.1) $P/(1-P)$ is undefined.

The number of previous arrests will clearly increase the probability of conviction. It is often argued that a well-educated white person with a high income is likely to be acquited or released on probation. If this perception is valid, the probability of conviction will decrease when education and income increase or when a person is white. In principle, the gender should be irrelevant to the probability of conviction.

EX 12.7

This is an example of the Tobit model. The model is

$$W = \beta_o + \beta_1 AGE + \beta_2 EDUC + \beta_3 EXP + \beta_4 RACE + \beta_5 CLER + \beta_6 PROF + u$$

for those who are employed, and $W = 0$ for others. AGE is the age, EDUC is education, EXP is experience, $RACE = 1$ for white, $CLER = 1$ for a clerical worker, and $PROF = 1$ for a professional work. The unskilled group is the control. The maximum likelihood procedure will be applied here to a likelihood function similar to the one in Section 12.4.

CHAPTER 13

PRACTICE PROBLEMS

PP 13.1

Substituting equations (13.4) through (13.6) in (13.7) we get,

$$Y_t = \alpha_0 + \alpha_1(Y_t - T_t) + \alpha_2(Y_{t-1} - T_{t-1}) + u_t + \beta_0 + \beta_1(Y_t - T_t) + \beta_2(Y_{t-1} - T_{t-1}) + v_t$$

Regrouping terms, this becomes

$$(1-\alpha_1-\beta_1)Y_t = \alpha_0 + (\alpha_2+\beta_2)Y_{t-1} - (\alpha_1+\beta_1)T_t - (\alpha_2+\beta_2)T_{t-1} + G_t + u_t + v_t$$

The reduced form equation for Y_t is therefore given by

$$Y_t = \frac{\alpha_0}{1-\alpha_1-\beta_1} + \frac{\alpha_2+\beta_2}{1-\alpha_1-\beta_1}Y_{t-1} - \frac{\alpha_1+\beta_1}{1-\alpha_1-\beta_1}T_t - \frac{\alpha_2+\beta_2}{1-\alpha_1-\beta_1}T_{t-1} + \frac{G_t+u_t+v_t}{1-\alpha_1-\beta_1}$$

$$= \pi_0 + \pi_1 Y_{t-1} + \pi_2 T_t + \pi_3 T_{t-1} + \pi_4 G_t + error$$

The other reduced form equations are easily derived from this.

PP 13.2

It will be noted that the second and third equations are self-contained and do not have Y_1. They can be solved jointly for Y_2 and Y_3. Substituting for Y_2 from the second equation into the third equation, we can solve for Y_3 as

$$Y_3 = \frac{\gamma_0+\gamma_1\beta_0}{1-\gamma_1\beta_1} + \frac{\gamma_1\beta_2}{1-\gamma_1\beta_1}X_1 + error = \theta_0 + \theta_1 X_1 + error$$

Using this in the second equation and grouping terms, we get

$$Y_2 = (\beta_0+\beta_1\theta_0) + (\beta_1\theta_1+\beta_2)X_1 + error$$

$$= \mu_0 + \mu_1 X_1 + error$$

Next, substitute for Y_2 and Y_3 in the first equation.

$$Y_1 = \alpha_0 + \alpha_1(\mu_0 + \mu_1 X_1) + \alpha_2(\theta_0 + \theta_1 X_1) + \alpha_4 X_1 + \alpha_5 X_2 + error$$

Solving for the reduced form for Y_1, we get

$$\begin{aligned} Y_1 &= (\alpha_0 + \alpha_1\mu_0 + \alpha_2\theta_0) + (\alpha_1\mu_1 + \alpha_2\theta_1 + \alpha_4)X_1 + \alpha_5 X_2 + error \\ &= \lambda_0 + \lambda_1 X_1 + \lambda_2 X_2 + error \end{aligned}$$

EXERCISES

EX 13.2

From Section 13.5 the ILS estimate of β is given by $\tilde{\beta} = S_{CI}/(S_{CI} + S_{II})$. Applying OLS to the reduced form equation for Y_t, we get $\hat{\mu}_1 = S_{YI}/S_{II}$ by proceeding as we did in Chapter 3. From equation (13.14) we see that $\hat{\mu}_1 = 1/(1-\hat{\beta})$. Hence the ILS estimate is

$$\hat{\beta} = \frac{\hat{\mu}_1 - 1}{\hat{\mu}_1} = \frac{S_{YI} - S_{II}}{S_{YI}}$$

Because $Y = C + I$, we have

$$S_{YI} = \Sigma(Y - \bar{Y})(I - \bar{I}) = \Sigma\left[(C - \bar{C}) + (I - \bar{I})\right](I - \bar{I}) = S_{CI} + S_{II}$$

Hence $\hat{\beta} = (S_{YI} - S_{II})/S_{YI} = S_{CI}/(S_{CI} + S_{II})$, which is the same as $\tilde{\beta}$. Therefore ILS can be applied to the reduced form of either C_t or Y_t.

EX 13.4

(a) Because these are three endogenous variables, at least two variables must be absent in each equation. In the second equation A and X are absent. In the third equation M, Y, and U are excluded. The third equation is therefore over-identified. The second equation is exactly identified.

(b) The equation for M is already in the reduced form. We have

$$A = X - M = (\beta_1 - \alpha_1) - \alpha_2 Y + (\beta_2 - \alpha_3)P + \beta_3 A - \alpha_4 U + v - u$$

Solving for A we get the reduce form for A as

$$A = \frac{\beta_1 - \alpha_1}{1-\beta_3} - \frac{\alpha_2 Y}{1-\beta_3} + \frac{\beta_2 - \alpha_3}{1-\beta_3} P - \frac{\alpha_4 U}{1-\beta_3} + \frac{v - u}{1-\beta_3}$$

The reduced form for X is

$$X = \beta_1 + \beta_2 P + \beta_3 \left[\frac{\beta_1 - \alpha_1}{1-\beta_3} - \frac{\alpha_2 Y}{1-\beta_3} + \frac{\beta_2 - \alpha_3}{1-\beta_3} P - \frac{\alpha_4 U}{1-\beta_3} + \frac{v-u}{1-\beta_3} \right] + v$$

$$= \frac{\beta_1 - \beta_3 \alpha_1}{1-\beta_3} + \frac{\beta_2 - \beta_3 \alpha_3}{1-\beta_3} P - \frac{\beta_3 \alpha_2}{1-\beta_3} Y - \frac{\beta_3 \alpha_4 U}{1-\beta_3} + \frac{v - \beta_3 u}{1-\beta_3}$$

(c) First regress A against a constant, Y, P, and U, and save $\hat{A}$. Next regress X against a constant P, and $\hat{A}$ to obtain $\hat{\beta}_1, \hat{\beta}_2$, and $\hat{\beta}_3$.

(d) The second equation has no other endogenous variables and is hence already in the reduced form. Therefore OLS will give estimates which are unbiased, consistent, and efficient.

(e) Because A is correlated with v, OLS estimates of the third equation will be biased and inconsistent.

EX 13.5

(a) If homes are expensive, they are targets for burglaries and hence property crime can be expected to increase (that is, $\alpha_2 > 0$). If POPDEN is high, there are two effects. There may be more houses to burgle and hence POP-CRIME might go up. But if an area is dense, more people might be alert and report crimes. The sign of α_3 is therefore ambiguous. If unemployment rate is high more people might turn to crime ($\alpha_4 > 0$). If more police are around, crime is likely to be less ($\alpha_5 < 0$, and $\beta_2 < 0$). Death penalty is likely to reduce violent crimes ($\beta_3 < 0$). The effect of age is ambiguous. If crime is up, a municipality is likely to hire more police officers. Hence we would expect γ_2 and γ_3 to be positive.

(b) We need two variables to be absent from each equation. The first equation has DEATH, MEDAGE, and VIOLNTCRIME missing. The second equation has MEDHOME, POPDEN, UNEMP, and PROPCRIME missing. The third equation has MEDHOME, POPDEN, UNEMP, DEATH, and MEDAGE missing. The order condition is therefore satisfied by all equations.

(c) First regress each of POLICE, PROPCRIME, and VIOLNTCRIME against a constant, MEDHOME, POPDEN, UNEMP, DEATH, and MEDAGE, and save the predicted values. In the second stage use these predicted values in place of the actual values and estimate the three equations. In obtaining residuals and standard errors however, actual values will be used. Thus

$$\hat{w} = POLICE - \hat{\gamma}_1 - \hat{\gamma}_2\ PROPCRIME - \hat{\gamma}_3\ VIOLNTCRIME$$

EX 13.6

Substituting for y_1 from the first equation into the second and solving for y_2, we get

$$y_2 = \frac{\beta_1\alpha_2}{1-\alpha_1\beta_1}x_1 + \frac{\beta_2}{1-\alpha_1\beta_1}x_2 + \frac{\beta_3}{1-\alpha_1\beta_1}x_3 + \frac{\beta_1 u + v}{1-\alpha_1\beta_1}$$

$$= \pi_1 x_1 + \pi_2 x_2 + \pi_3 x_3 + \varepsilon_1$$

Substituting this into the first equation, we have

$$y_1 = (\alpha_1\pi_1 + \alpha_2)x_1 + \alpha_1\pi_2 x_2 + \alpha_1\pi_3 x_3 + \varepsilon_2$$

Note that $\mu_2 = \alpha_1\pi_2$ and $\mu_3 = \alpha_1\pi_3$. Hence, α_1 can be estimated two ways as $\hat{\mu}_2/\hat{\pi}_2$ and as $\hat{\mu}_3/\hat{\pi}_3$. Thus the model is overidentified and the appropriate estimation procedure is TSLS. In the first stage, regress y_1 and y_2 against x_1, x_2, and x_3 and compute $\hat{y}_1$ and $\hat{y}_2$. Next estimate the two structural equations using $\hat{y}_i$ instead of y_i $(i = 1,2)$.

EX 13.7

Substituting for y_2 from the second equation into the first and solving for y_1, we get

$$y_1 = (\alpha_1\beta_1 + \alpha_2)\ x_1 + \alpha_1\beta_2 x_2 + (u + \alpha_1 v)$$

If u and v are uncorrelated with x_1 and x_2, then the error terms are well behaved hence there is no simultaneous equation bias. OLS is therefore appropriate.

EX 13.8

Here also since u_t and v_t are uncorrelated with the explanatory variables, all assumptions made in Chapter 3 about the error terms hold and hence there is no simultaneous equation bias. OLS is therefore appropriate here also.

EX 13.9

The following ESL commands will be useful in obtaining the empirical results for this exercise.

```
genr TAXt=100*GOVREC/Pt
(* generate disposable income *)
genr DISPINCM=GDP-TAXt
(* generate real money supply *)
genr M=100*MONYSUP/Pt
(* generate per capita measures *)
genr Yt=GDP
genr Ct=CONS
genr It=INV
genr Gt=GOVEXP
genr Tt=TAXt
genr Xt=EXPORTS
genr IMPt=IMPORTS
genr DYt=DISPINCM
genr Mt=M
lags Yt Ct It Gt Xt DYt Mt rt ;
smpl 1960 1993;
(* TSLS estimation *)
tsls Ct 0 Ct_1 DYt DYt_1; 0 Ct_1 DYt_1 It_1 Yt_1 rt_1 Mt
   Mt_1 Gt Xt;
tsls It 0 It_1 Yt Yt_1 rt rt_1 ; 0 Ct_1 DYt_1 It_1 Yt_1
   rt_1 Mt Mt_1 Gt Xt;
tsls rt 0 rt_1 Yt Yt_1 Mt Mt_1; 0 Ct_1 DYt_1 It_1 Yt_1
   rt_1 Mt Mt_1 Gt Xt;
tsls rt 0 rt_1 Yt_1 Mt Mt_1; 0 Ct_1 DYt_1 It_1 Yt_1 rt_1
   Mt Mt_1 Gt Xt;
tsls Tt 0 Yt ; 0 Ct_1 DYt_1 It_1 Yt_1 rt_1 Mt Mt_1 Gt Xt;
tsls IMPt 0 Yt ; 0 Ct_1 DYt_1 It_1 Yt_1 rt_1 Mt Mt_1 Gt Xt ;
```

The estimated relations (without the summary statistics) are given below.

$$\hat{C}_t = -67.2643 + 0.8208\, C_{t-1} + 0.7563\, DY_t - 0.5552\, DY_{t-1}$$

$$\hat{I}_t = -48.0053 + 0.5022\, I_{t-1} + 0.6644\, Y_t - 0.5947\, Y_{t-1}$$

$$+ 16.3744\, r_t - 12.2292\, r_{t-1}$$

$$\hat{r}_t = 2.2018 + 1.1717\, r_{t-1} - 0.00222\, Y_{t-1} - 0.0135\, M_t + 0.0157\, M_{t-1}$$

$$\hat{T}_t = -125.2768 + 0.3344\, Y_t$$

$$I\hat{M}Pt = -311.8575 + 0.1757\, Y_t$$

The corresponding long-run structural relations are given below.

$$\hat{C}^* = -375.3588 + 1.1222\,(Y^* - T^*)$$

$$\hat{I}^* = -96.4349 + 0.14\, Y^* + 8.327\, r^*$$

$$\hat{r}^* = -12.8235 + 0.01293\, Y^* - 0.0128\, M^*$$

As in the case in Section 13.6, we have several counterintuitive results. For instance, the long-run marginal propensity to consume is greater than one, which is unacceptable. Also, in the investment equation interest rate has a positive. The results are thus qualitatively similar to the model in per capita terms and suggests misspecification.

EX 13.10

Use the following ESL commands to obtain the empirical results for this exercise.

```
genr TAXt=100*GOVREC/Pt
(* generate disposable income *)
genr DISPINCM=GDP-TAXt
(* generate real money supply *)
genr M=100*MONYSUP/Pt
(* generate per capita measures *)
genr Yt=GDP/POP
genr Ct=CONS/POP
genr It=INV/POP
genr Gt=GOVEXP/POP
genr Tt=TAXt/POP
genr Xt=EXPORTS/POP
genr IMPt=IMPORTS/POP
genr DYt=DISPINCM/POP
```

```
genr Mt=M/POP
lags Yt Ct It Gt Xt DYt Mt rt ;
genr DYt_2 = DYt(-2)
genr Yt_2 = Yt(-2)
genr Ct_2 = Ct(-2)
genr It_2 = It(-2)
genr Mt_2 = Mt(-2)
genr rt_2 = rt(-2)
smpl 1961 1993;
(* TSLS estimation *)
tsls Ct 0 Ct_1 Ct_2 DYt DYt_1 DYt_2 ; 0 Ct_1 Ct_2 DYt_1
   DYt_2 It_1 It_2 Yt_1 Yt_2 rt_1 rt_2 Mt Mt_1 Mt_2 Gt Xt;
tsls It 0 It_1 It_2 Yt Yt_1 Yt_2 rt rt_1 rt_2 ; 0 Ct_1
   Ct_2 DYt_1 DYt_2 It_1 It_2 Yt_1 Yt_2 rt_1 rt_2 Mt
   Mt_1 Mt_2 Gt Xt;
tsls rt 0 rt_1 rt_2 Yt Yt_1 Yt_2 Mt Mt_1 Mt_2 ; 0 Ct_1
   Ct_2 DYt_1 DYt_2 It_1 It_2 Yt_1 Yt_2 rt_1 rt_2 Mt
   Mt_1 Mt_2 Gt Xt;
tsls Tt 0 Yt Yt_1 ; 0 Ct_1 Ct_2 DYt_1 DYt_2 It_1 It_2
   Yt_1 Yt_2 rt_1 rt_2 Mt Mt_1 Mt_2 Gt Xt;
tsls IMPt 0 Yt Yt_1 ; 0 Ct_1 Ct_2 DYt_1 DYt_2 It_1 It_2
   Yt_1 Yt_2 rt_1 rt_2 Mt Mt_1 Mt_2 Gt Xt;
```

The results indicate that the only case in which the added lagged terms appear significantly is the tax equation. In it, one period lagged GDP is significant. In all other cases, the added terms are insignificant. This suggests that autocorrelation may not be a serious problem, possibly because the lagged dependent variables are indirectly allowing for it.